WORKBOOK

A Six-Session, Video-Based Study for Small Groups or Individuals

LOVE THE WORD. LEARN THE WORD. LIVE THE WORD.

RICK WARREN

40 Days in the Word Workbook
Love the Word. Learn the Word. Live the Word.

Edition 2.0

PASTORRICK.COM

Published by Purpose Driven Publishers
23182 Arroyo Vista
Rancho Santa Margarita, CA 92688

ISBN: 978-1-4228-0179-6

Printed in Korea.

PX370001-20230104

TABLE of CONTENTS

A NOTE from RICK WARREN

Welcome to *40 Days in the Word*. I am so glad you have decided to join me for this journey together. No other habit can do more to transform your life and make you more like Jesus than to study and act upon God's Word. To be a healthy disciple of Jesus, feeding on God's Word must be your first priority. Jesus called it "abiding." He said, *"If you [abide] in my word, then you are truly disciples of mine"* (John 8:31 NASB).

By the end of our forty days together, my goal is to help you . . .

- Love the Word of God like you've never loved it before
- Learn the Word of God like you've never learned it before
- Live the Word of God like you've never lived it before

God's Word is not meant just to inform you, but to transform you. God never meant for Bible study to simply increase our knowledge. Receiving, reading, researching, remembering, and reflecting on the Bible is useless if we fail to put God's Word into practice. The apostle James says if we want our lives to be blessed by God, we must become *"doers of the word"* (James 1:22 KJV).

Jesus says both knowing and applying the Word creates the foundation for our lives: *"Everyone who hears these words of mine and puts them into practice is like a wise man who built his house on the rock"* (Matthew 7:24 NIV). In order to become Christlike, we must become living translations of God's Word.

God's Word is unlike any other book. It is alive. When God speaks, your life will be transformed, but that can only happen by making the Bible the authoritative standard for your life: the compass you rely on for direction, the counsel you listen to for making wise decisions, and the benchmark you use for evaluating everything. The Bible must always have the first and last word in your life.

My hope is that the next forty days will become the most important days of your life as you love God's Word, learn God's Word, and live God's Word.

UNDERSTANDING Your WORKBOOK

Here is a brief explanation of the features of this workbook.

Looking Ahead / Catching Up: You will open each meeting by briefly discussing a question or two that will help focus everyone's attention on the subject of the lesson.

Memory Verse: Each week you will find a key Bible verse for your group to memorize together. If someone in the group has a different translation, ask them to read it aloud so the group can get a bigger picture of the meaning of the passage.

Video Lesson: There is a **Video Lesson** for the group to watch together each week. Fill in the blanks in the lesson outlines as you watch the video and be sure to refer back to these outlines during your discussion time.

Discovery Questions: Each video segment is complemented by several questions for group discussion. Please don't feel pressured to discuss every single question. There is no reason to rush through the answers. Give everyone ample opportunity to share their thoughts. If you don't get through all of the discussion questions, that's okay.

Putting It Into Practice: ***The Micah 6:8 Assignment*** is where the rubber meets the road. We don't want to be just hearers of the Word. We also need to be doers of the Word (James 1:22). ***The Micah 6:8 Assignment*** is an application exercise that will help your group put the Word of God into practice.

Living on Purpose: This section contains your daily quiet time instructions that will enable you to practice the study methods Pastor Rick is teaching each week. By following this plan in the next 40 days, you will read and meditate on *The Book of Philippians*, *The Gospel of Mark*, *The Book of James*, and Psalm 1.

Prayer Direction: At the end of each session you will find suggestions for your group prayer time. Praying together is one of the greatest privileges of small group life. Please don't take it for granted.

Diving Deeper: If you want to go deeper in your personal Bible study, read the materials recommended in this section. You will find them in the back of your workbook.

Journal Pages: There are seven **Journal Pages** at the end of each session in your workbook to help you with your **Living on Purpose** daily devotions.

A Tip for the Host

The group discussion material is meant to be your servant, not your master. The point is not to race through the sessions; the point is to take time to let God work in your lives. Nor is it necessary to "go around the circle" before you move on to the next question. Give people the freedom to speak, but don't insist on it. Your group will enjoy deeper, more open sharing and discussion if people don't feel pressured to speak up.

Session One
PRONOUNCE IT!

LOOKING AHEAD

- If this is a new group, take a few minutes to introduce yourselves. Be sure to review the **Small Group Guidelines** on page 192 of this workbook.
- What are your first memories of the Bible?

___

___

___

___

- What are you hoping to get out of this study?

___

___

___

___

___

MEMORY VERSE

Let the word of Christ dwell in you richly.

Colossians 3:16 (NIV)

Watch the **Video Lesson** now and take notes in your outline. Refer back to the outline during your group discussion.

PRONOUNCE IT!

The ultimate purpose of the Bible is not to inform us; it is to transform us. God doesn't want us to just be hearers of the Word, he wants us to be doers of the Word—living Gospels—sharing the Good News of Jesus Christ not only in our words, but in our lives.

> ***All Scripture is given by inspiration of God, and is profitable for doctrine, for reproof, for correction, [and] for instruction in righteousness, [so] that the man of God may be complete, thoroughly equipped for every good work.***
>
> 2 Timothy 3:16–17 (NKJV)

The ultimate purpose of the Bible is to ______________________________.

FIVE BASIC PRINCIPLES OF BIBLE STUDY

- **Ask the ______________________________.**
- **Write down ______________________________.**
- **Don't just interpret it, ______________________________.**

I only believe the parts of the Bible that ______________________________.

The real problem for most of us is not with interpreting difficult passages, but with obeying the passages we do understand.

- **Study it ______________________________.**
- **Read it ______________________________.**

You can summarize the devotional study method in one word:

________________________________ .

> ***"Do not let this Book of the Law depart from your mouth; meditate on it day and night, so that you may be careful to do everything written in it. Then you will be prosperous and successful."***
>
> Joshua 1:8 (NIV)

> ***Oh, how I love your law! I meditate on it all day long.***
>
> Psalm 119:97 (NIV)

> ***My eyes stay open through the watches of the night, that I may meditate on your promises.***
>
> Psalm 119:148 (NIV)

Biblical meditation is essentially thought digestion. Another word for biblical meditation is "rumination." Rumination is what a cow does when it chews its cud. Scriptural meditation is reading a passage over and over again, then thinking about it and concentrating on it in different ways until you have digested its meaning.

THE "PRONOUNCE IT!" METHOD OF BIBLE MEDITATION

Read the verse over and over again, but emphasize each word in the verse one at a time. After each word, stop and write down your thoughts, even if it's just a word or two.

Let the word of Christ dwell in you richly.

Colossians 3:16 (NIV)

LET the word of Christ dwell in you richly.

____

Let the ***WORD*** of Christ dwell in you richly.

____

Let the word of ***CHRIST*** dwell in you richly.

____

Let the word of Christ ***DWELL*** in you richly.

____

Let the word of Christ dwell ***IN*** you richly.

____

Let the word of Christ dwell in ***YOU*** richly.

____

Let the word of Christ dwell in you ***RICHLY***.

____

Now look at your life through the lens of this verse. How does this truth apply to your life today? What are you going to do about it? After you have thought about an application, write it down. Then finish your time by talking to God about what he said to you in his Word.

Your time in daily devotions is not just for your benefit. It's also for the benefit of others.

DISCOVERY QUESTIONS

A Note to Your Group

You don't have to answer every question. Be sure to save enough time to discuss the **Putting It Into Practice** section of the study.

- As a group, practice the **Pronounce It!** method of Bible meditation using the first phrase of Colossians 3:15:

Let the peace of Christ rule in your hearts.

Colossians 3:15 (NIV)

- Which word has the most meaning for you? Why did you choose that word?

- How does this verse apply to your life right now? What do you need to do or stop doing in order to more fully experience the rulership of Christ's peace?

- Your time in daily devotions is not just for your benefit. It's also for the benefit of others. With whom do you need to share the lessons you just learned about the peace of Christ?

PUTTING IT INTO PRACTICE

The Micah 6:8 Assignment

- As a group, practice the **Pronounce It!** method on Micah 6:8. Talk about what these words mean to you.

> ***He has shown you, O [man], what is good. And what does the LORD require of you? To act justly and to love mercy and to walk humbly with your God.***
>
> Micah 6:8 (NIV)

- What can your group do to put this verse into practice? We don't want *40 Days in the Word* to just be a knowledge-based study. It is meant to be application-based. We want to put into practice the lessons God is teaching us in Scripture. The Bible says: *"Do not merely listen to the word, and so deceive yourselves. Do what it says"* (James 1:22 NIV).

In the next 40 days, your small group will select, plan, and initiate a group outreach project that we are calling ***The Micah 6:8 Assignment***. This might be a church-wide project involving all of the small groups in your congregation, or a project just for your group to take on. The nature and scope of the project is up to you. It could be a food drive for a local food bank, a clothing drive for the needy in your community, or volunteering at a homeless shelter. It could involve an orphan care project, an elderly care project, or partnering with a prison ministry. You don't have to decide today, but get started talking about what it could be.

Your project will become a major focus for your group over the next 40 days. Here are your next steps:

1. Recruit a group member to be your Micah 6:8 Champion. Your Champion will help keep everybody moving forward with your project.

   Our Micah 6:8 Champion is: ______________________________

2. Have the Micah 6:8 Champion go to **www.40daysintheword.com** and click on ***The Micah 6:8 Assignment*** link to find examples and ideas for a project for your group to undertake. Your Champion can report back to the group at your next meeting.

LIVING ON PURPOSE

During *40 Days in the Word*, you will be reading about one chapter a day in the Bible. You may read at your own pace, but we suggest you apply each week's method of Bible meditation to that day's recommended verse or passage.

This week in your daily quiet time, read *The Book of Philippians*. It's just four chapters long. There is no need to rush your way through the book. Remember, it's not how much of the Bible you get through every day; it's how deeply the Bible gets through to you. So take your time.

As you read each day, practice the **Pronounce It!** method using the seven recommended verses below from Philippians. Be sure to write down your thoughts and observations about how each verse applies to your life. You will find seven **Journal Pages** at the end of this session in your workbook to help you with your devotions.

DAY 1: ***Being confident of this, that he who began a good work in you will carry it on to completion until the day of Christ Jesus.***

Philippians 1:6 (NIV)

DAY 2: ***Whatever happens, conduct yourselves in a manner worthy of the gospel of Christ.***

Philippians 1:27 (NIV)

DAY 3: ***For God is working in you, giving you the desire and the power to do what pleases him.***

Philippians 2:13 (NLT)

DAY 4: ***I press on to take hold of that for which Christ Jesus took hold of me.***

Philippians 3:12 (NIV)

DAY 5: ***Do not be anxious about anything, but in everything, by prayer and petition, with thanksgiving, present your requests to God.***

Philippians 4:6 (NIV)

DAY 6: ***I can do all things through Christ who strengthens me.***

Philippians 4:13 (NKJV)

DAY 7: ***My God will meet all your needs according to his glorious riches in Christ Jesus.***

Philippians 4:19 (NIV)

If you miss a day, don't let that discourage you. Just pick up with the current day and keep moving forward. Don't let yesterday's famine rob today of its feast.

PRAYER DIRECTION

- Take a few minutes to pray for each other's prayer requests. We suggest you recruit one of your group members to record prayer requests and answers to prayer, using the **Small Group Prayer and Praise Report** on page 196 of this workbook. Any volunteers?
- Pray for God's direction for your group's ***Micah 6:8 Assignment***.

DIVING DEEPER

If you have questions about the Bible itself—such as: *How do we know the Bible came from God?* or *How do I know I can trust the Bible?* or *How do we know we have the right books?*—read the bonus chapter titled, ***Foundations: The Bible*** on page 125 of this workbook.

GREAT RESOURCES FOR YOUR DEVOTIONAL LIFE

Be sure to visit **www.40daysintheword.com** where you can:

- Register for Pastor Rick's Daily Hope email devotions. They're free!
- Download the free daily audio devotions for *40 Days in the Word*.
- Learn more about beginning, intermediate, and advanced tools, links, and resources for in-depth Bible study.

Pronounce It!

Being confident of this, that he who began a good work in you will carry it on to completion until the day of Christ Jesus.

Philippians 1:6 (NIV)

Read the entire verse several times, stopping after each word to write down your thoughts.

Apply It!

How does this verse apply to your life and what will you do about it?

Your prayer . . .

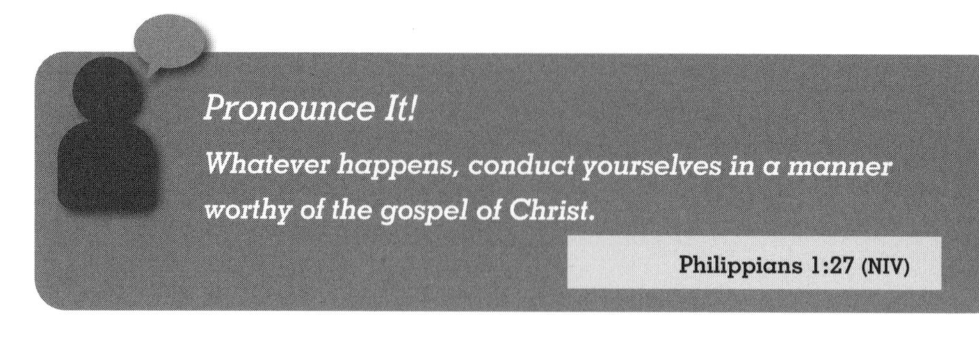

Pronounce It!

Whatever happens, conduct yourselves in a manner worthy of the gospel of Christ.

Philippians 1:27 (NIV)

Read the entire verse several times, stopping after each word to write down your thoughts.

Apply It!

How does this verse apply to your life and what will you do about it?

Your prayer . . .

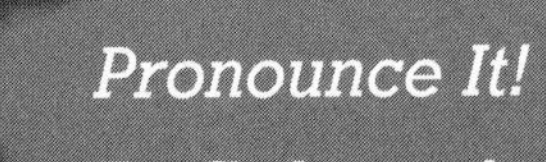

Pronounce It!

For God is working in you, giving you the desire and the power to do what pleases him.

Philippians 2:13 (NLT)

Read the entire verse several times, stopping after each word to write down your thoughts.

Apply It!

How does this verse apply to your life and what will you do about it?

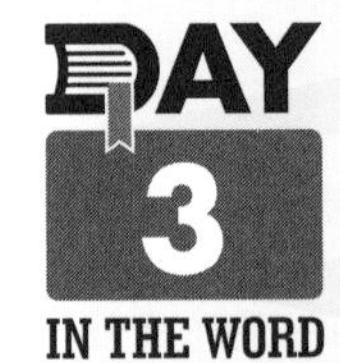

Your prayer . . .

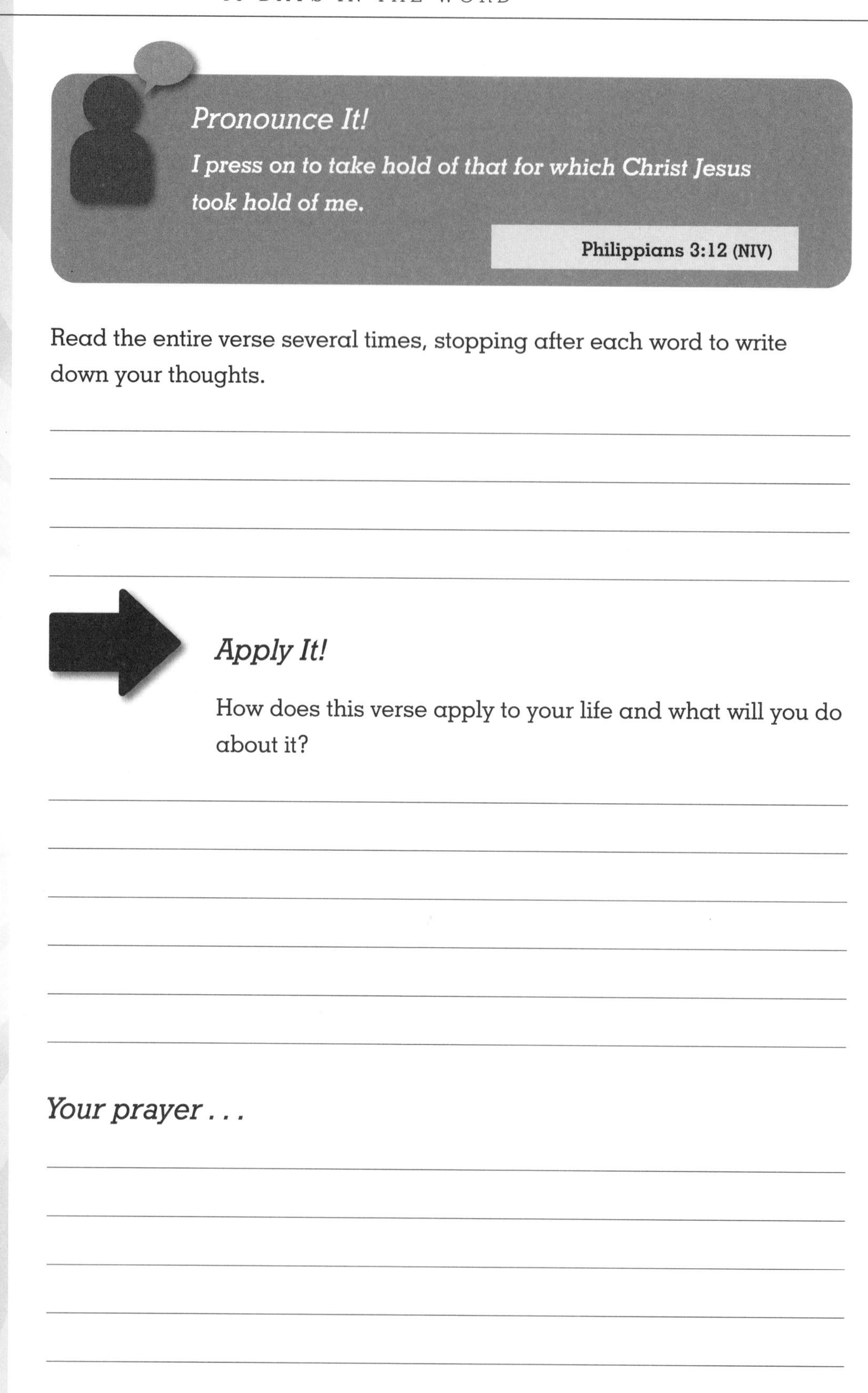

Pronounce It!

I press on to take hold of that for which Christ Jesus took hold of me.

Philippians 3:12 (NIV)

Read the entire verse several times, stopping after each word to write down your thoughts.

Apply It!

How does this verse apply to your life and what will you do about it?

DAY 4 IN THE WORD

Your prayer . . .

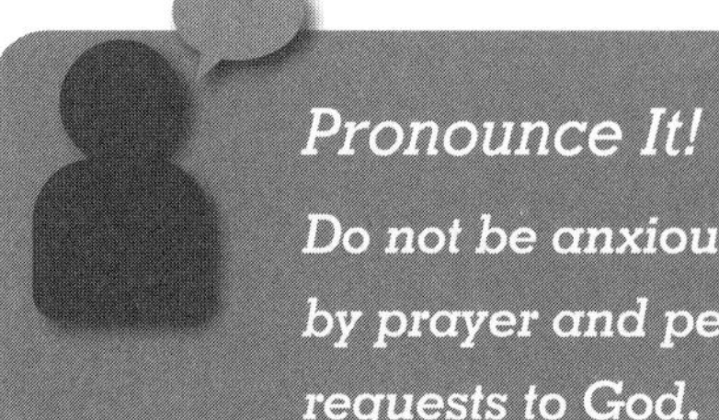

Pronounce It!

Do not be anxious about anything, but in everything, by prayer and petition, with thanksgiving, present your requests to God.

Philippians 4:6 (NIV)

Read the entire verse several times, stopping after each word to write down your thoughts.

Apply It!

How does this verse apply to your life and what will you do about it?

Your prayer . . .

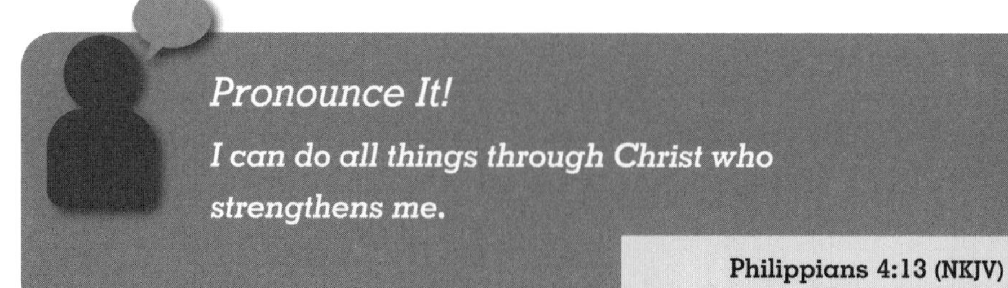

Read the entire verse several times, stopping after each word to write down your thoughts.

Apply It!

How does this verse apply to your life and what will you do about it?

Your prayer . . .

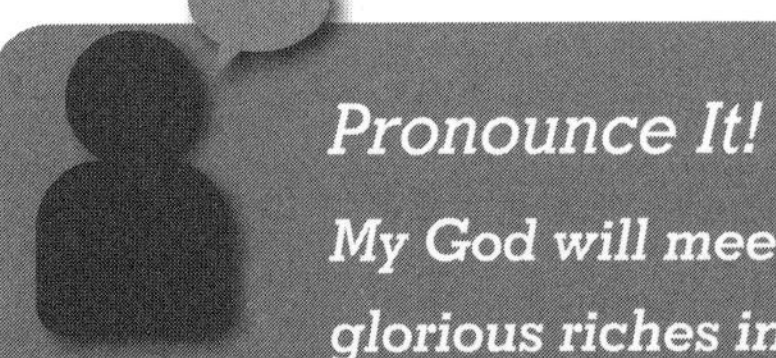

Pronounce It!

My God will meet all your needs according to his glorious riches in Christ Jesus.

Philippians 4:19 (NIV)

Read the entire verse several times, stopping after each word to write down your thoughts.

Apply It!

How does this verse apply to your life and what will you do about it?

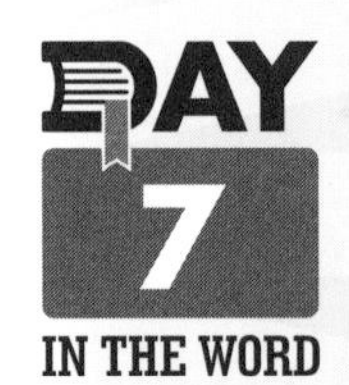

Your prayer . . .

Session Two
PICTURE IT!

CATCHING UP

- Would anyone like to share an insight you gained in Philippians by practicing the **Pronounce It!** method in your daily quiet time?

- Would you rather read the book or see the movie?

MEMORY VERSE

Open my eyes that I may see wonderful things in your law.

Psalm 119:18 (NIV)

Watch the **Video Lesson** now and take notes in your outline. Refer back to the outline during your group discussion.

PICTURE IT!

Every person in the world has exactly the same amount of time each week: 168 hours. You don't have time for everything; you have to make time for things that really count.

> *"Seek first his kingdom and his righteousness, and all these things will be given to you as well."*
>
> Matthew 6:33 (NIV)

FOUR PRIVILEGES OF A QUIET TIME

- **We give ______________________ to God.**
  - **God ______________________ our devotion.**
  - **God ______________________ our devotion.**

> *"Here I am! I stand at the door and knock. If anyone hears my voice and opens the door, I will come in and eat with him, and he with me."*
>
> Revelation 3:20 (NIV)

- **We get ______________________ from God.**

> *Show me your ways, O Lord, teach me your paths; guide me in your truth and teach me, for you are God my Savior, and my hope is in you all day long.*
>
> Psalm 25:4-5 (NIV)

Trust in the Lord with all your heart and lean not on your own understanding; in all your ways acknowledge him, and he will make your paths straight.

Proverbs 3:5–6 (NIV)

- We gain ______________________________ in God.

You fill me with joy in your presence.

Psalm 16:11 (NIV)

I consider everything a loss compared to the surpassing greatness of knowing Christ Jesus my Lord.

Philippians 3:8 (NIV)

- We grow ______________________________ God.

FOUR ESSENTIAL ELEMENTS OF A QUIET TIME

- Start with the proper ______________________________ .

The Lord does not look at the things man looks at. Man looks at the outward appearance, but the Lord looks at the heart.

1 Samuel 16:7 (NIV)

- Come with ______________________________ .
- Come with ______________________________ .
- Come with ______________________________ .
- Come with ______________________________ to obey.

- Select a specific ________________.
    - The best time is when you ________________.
- Choose a special ________________.

Jesus went out as usual to the Mount of Olives, and his disciples followed him.

Luke 22:39 (NIV)

- Follow a simple ________________.

SIX STEPS FOR A QUIET TIME

- Wait ________________.
- Pray ________________.

Search me, O God, and know my heart; test me and know my anxious thoughts. See if there is any offensive way in me, and lead me in the way everlasting.

Psalm 139:23–24 (NIV)

Open my eyes that I may see wonderful things in your law.

Psalm 119:18 (NIV)

- Read ________________.
- ________________ and ________________.
- Write down ________________.
- Have ________________.

Give all your worries and cares to God, for he cares about you.

1 Peter 5:7 (NLT)

THE "PICTURE IT!" METHOD OF BIBLE MEDITATION

This method works best when you're reading a narrative passage, story, or parable.

- Try to picture the biblical scene in your mind. See yourself as one of the active participants. Ask yourself, "How would I feel if I were involved in this situation? What would I say? What would I do?" Then see yourself as a different character in the story and ask yourself the same questions again.
- Next, ask yourself, "With whom in the story do I identify most, and how does their situation apply to my life right now? What is God trying to say to me? What does he want me to do?"
- Then take a few minutes to write down your thoughts, observations, questions, and any action steps you need to take.

When you start picturing a scene, Scripture comes tremendously alive to you and you see it in a whole new light.

DISCOVERY QUESTIONS

A Note to Your Group

You don't have to answer every question. Be sure to save enough time to discuss the **Putting It Into Practice** section of the study.

As Pastor Rick suggested, practice the **Picture It!** method of Bible meditation, using the account of the paralytic from Mark 2.

A few days later, when Jesus again entered Capernaum, the people heard that he had come home. So many gathered that there was no room left, not even outside the door, and he preached the word to them. Some men came, bringing to him a paralytic, carried by four of them. Since they could not get him to Jesus because of the crowd, they made an opening in the roof above Jesus and, after digging through it, lowered the mat the paralyzed man was lying on. When Jesus saw their faith, he said to the paralytic, "Son, your sins are forgiven."

Now some teachers of the law were sitting there, thinking to themselves, "Why does this fellow talk like that? He's blaspheming! Who can forgive sins but God alone?"

Immediately Jesus knew in his spirit that this was what they were thinking in their hearts, and he said to them, "Why are you thinking these things? Which is easier: to say to the paralytic, 'Your sins are forgiven,' or to say, 'Get up, take your mat and walk'? But that you may know that the Son of Man has authority on earth to forgive sins . . ." He said to the paralytic, "I tell you, get up, take your mat and go home." He got up, took his mat and walked out in full view of them all. This amazed everyone and they praised God, saying, "We have never seen anything like this!"

Mark 2:1–12 (NIV)

Which of the people in the story do you most identify with? Have each member of your group choose one of the following:

- **Picture yourself as the man on the mat . . .**

  What must it be like to be so helpless? Is there an area of your life where you feel paralyzed right now—with fear, indecision, self-doubt, guilt, or sorrow? Who do you need to ask to help bring your need to Jesus in prayer?

- **Picture yourself as one of the men on the roof . . .**

  What kind of faith and determination did it take for them to do what they did? Who do you know that needs your help right now? Who needs you to pray for them? Who needs your help finding their way to Jesus? What is blocking the way?

- **Picture yourself as the homeowner . . .**

  Have you ever been inconvenienced by someone in need? In light of the man's healing, was it worth the trouble you were put through?

- **Picture yourself as one of the people in the crowd . . .**

  Why did you come to the house? How do you feel about the guy who just cut in line? What have you seen Jesus do in other people's lives and how has it strengthened your faith?

PUTTING IT INTO PRACTICE

The Micah 6:8 Assignment

- As a group, practice the **Picture It!** method using Micah 6:8. What does it look like to act justly, love mercy, and walk humbly with God?

> ***He has shown you, O [man], what is good. And what does the LORD require of you? To act justly and to love mercy and to walk humbly with your God.***
>
> Micah 6:8 (NIV)

____

____

____

- In our last session, we introduced you to ***The Micah 6:8 Assignment***, and asked you to recruit a Champion to visit **www.40daysintheword.com** and click on ***The Micah 6:8 Assignment*** link to get your group started. Here are the steps to take in this session:

1. Make a decision. Discuss your options and decide what your group's project will be.
2. Figure out a timeline. Decide the date. It would be great if you completed your project before the end of this series. How long will it take to plan? How much time will it require to implement? Is this a one-time activity or an on-going service opportunity?
3. Take inventory. What talents, abilities, experiences, resources, and relationships are available in your group to help meet the need you have selected?
4. Start getting organized. Measure the need. Determine what kinds of resources will be required. Make a plan. Divide up responsibilities and assign tasks.
5. What questions still need to be answered?
6. PRAY! We must always rely on the power of God to do the work of God.

LIVING ON PURPOSE

This week in your daily quiet time, read the first seven chapters of *The Gospel of Mark*. Using Pastor Rick's six steps for a quiet time, practice the **Picture It!** method with the recommended Scripture passages below. Be sure to write down your thoughts and observations about how each passage applies to your life. You will find seven **Journal Pages** at the end of this session in your workbook to help you with your devotions.

DAY 8:	Mark 1:40–45	***Jesus heals a leper***
DAY 9:	Mark 3:1–6	***Jesus heals a man with a shriveled hand***
DAY 10:	Mark 4:35–41	***Jesus calms the storm***
DAY 11:	Mark 5:21–43	***Jesus raises a dead girl and heals a sick woman***
DAY 12:	Mark 6:35–44	***Jesus feeds the 5,000***
DAY 13:	Mark 6:45–51	***Jesus walks on water***
DAY 14:	Mark 7:31–37	***Jesus heals a deaf and mute man***

If you miss a day, don't let that discourage you. Just pick up with the current day and keep moving forward. Don't let yesterday's famine rob today of its feast.

PRAYER DIRECTION

- Pray for each other's prayer requests. Use the **Small Group Prayer and Praise Report** on page 196 of this workbook to record prayer requests and answers to prayer.
- Pray about your group's ***Micah 6:8 Assignment***.

GREAT RESOURCES FOR YOUR DEVOTIONAL LIFE

Be sure to visit **www.40daysintheword.com**, where you can:

- Register for Pastor Rick's Daily Hope email devotions. They're free!
- Download the free daily audio devotions for *40 Days in the Word*.
- Learn more about beginning, intermediate, and advanced tools, links, and resources for in-depth Bible study.

Picture It!

Jesus heals a leper.

Mark 1:40–45

Put yourself in the story as each of the characters. With which character do you most relate?

Be the leper: What are you desperate for God to do in your life?

Be Jesus: Are you willing to touch "untouchable" people?

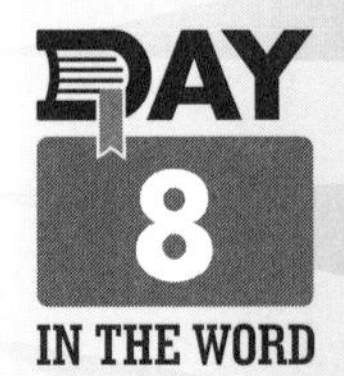

Apply It!

How does this passage apply to your life and what will you do about it?

Your prayer . . .

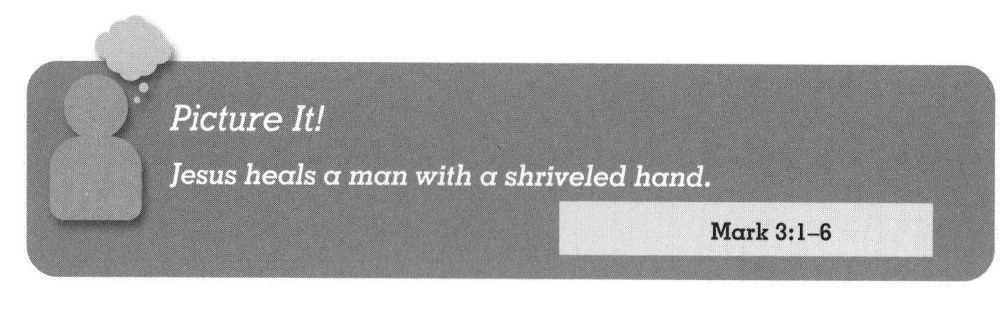

Put yourself in the story as each of the characters. With which character do you most relate?

Be the man with the shriveled hand: Are you incapacitated in any part of your life?

Be the Pharisee: Are you disturbed when Jesus breaks religious rules or does something out of the ordinary?

Apply It!

How does this passage apply to your life and what will you do about it?

Your prayer . . .

Put yourself in the story as each of the characters. With which character do you most relate?

Be a disciple: Has Jesus ever led you into a storm? Does it ever seem like he is asleep in the stern?

Be in one of the other boats (verse 36)**:** Have you ever been caught up in someone else's storm?

Apply It!

How does this passage apply to your life and what will you do about it?

Your prayer . . .

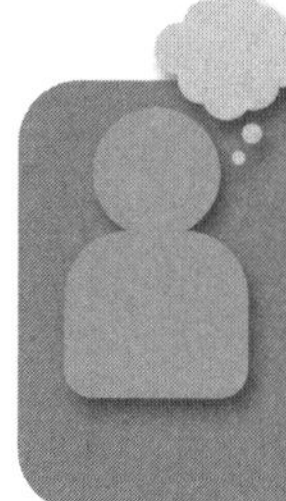

Picture It!

Jesus raises a dead girl and heals a sick woman.

Mark 5:21–43

Put yourself in the story as each of the characters. With which character do you most relate?

Be Jairus.

Be the woman.

Be the girl.

Be a disciple.

Apply It!

How does this passage apply to your life and what will you do about it?

Your prayer . . .

Picture It!

Jesus feeds the 5,000.

Mark 6:35–44

Put yourself in the story as each of the characters. With which character do you most relate?

Be a disciple.

Be a member of the crowd.

Be the boy (John 6:9).

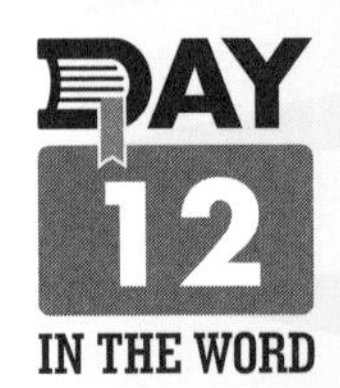

Apply It!

How does this passage apply to your life and what will you do about it?

Your prayer . . .

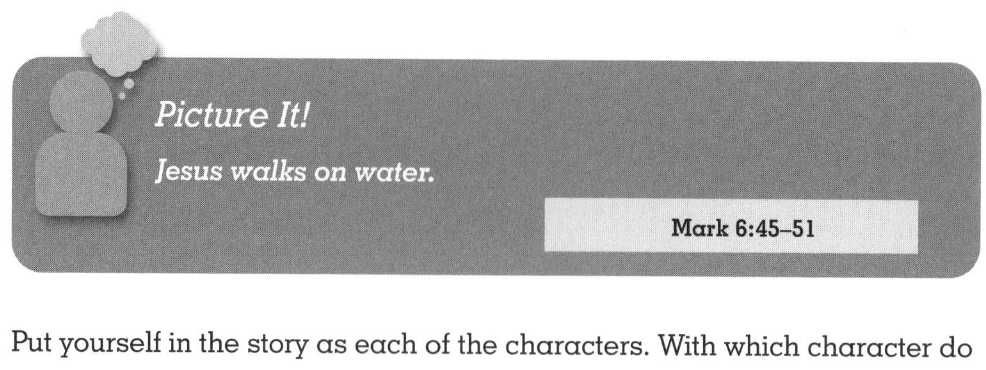

Put yourself in the story as each of the characters. With which character do you most relate?

Be a disciple in the boat.

Be Peter (Matthew 14:28–31).

Apply It!

How does this passage apply to your life and what will you do about it?

Your prayer . . .

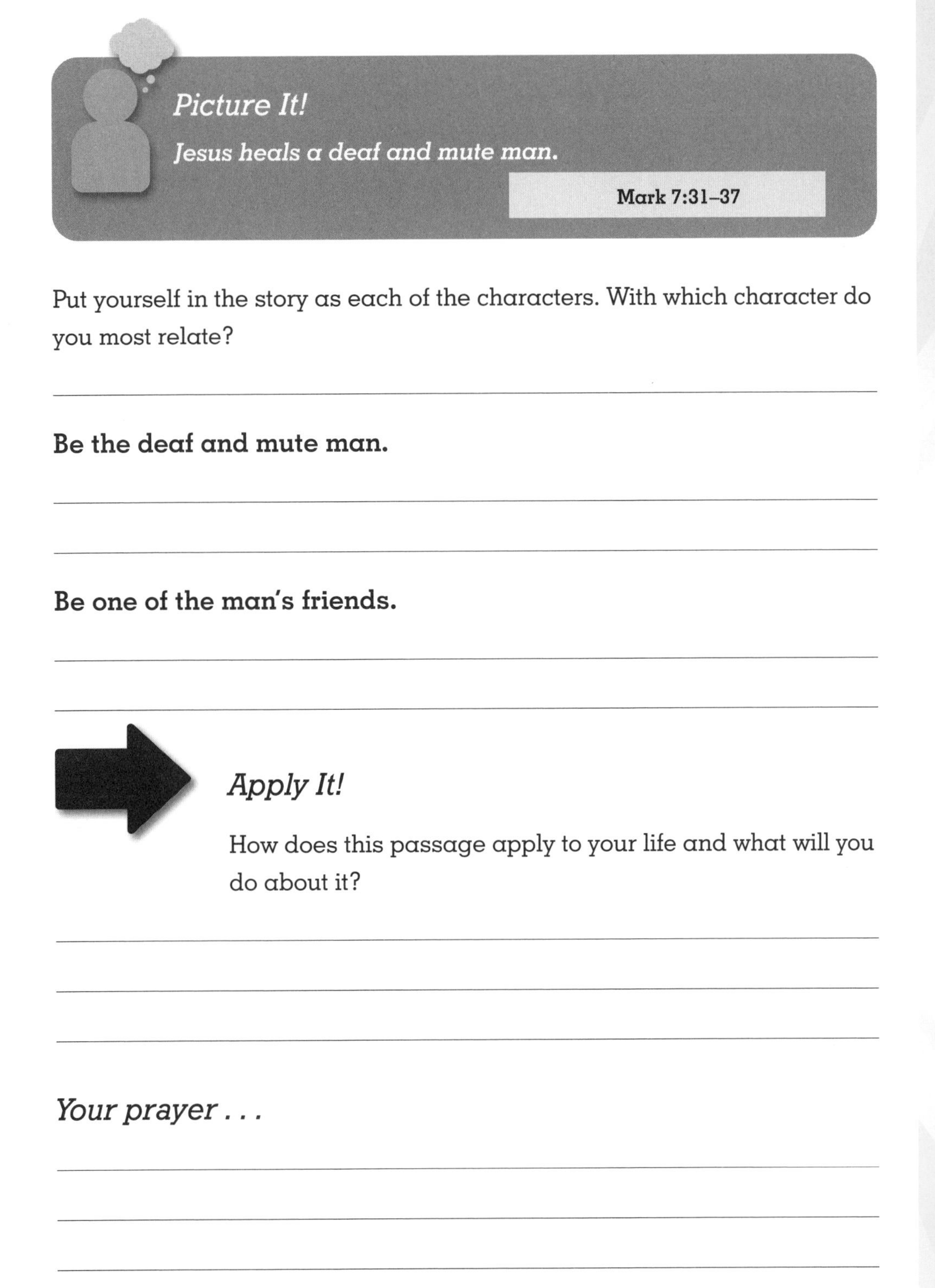

Picture It!

Jesus heals a deaf and mute man.

Mark 7:31–37

Put yourself in the story as each of the characters. With which character do you most relate?

Be the deaf and mute man.

Be one of the man's friends.

Apply It!

How does this passage apply to your life and what will you do about it?

Your prayer . . .

Session Three
PROBE IT!

CATCHING UP

- How did the **Picture It!** method make *The Gospel of Mark* come alive for you during your daily devotions this past week?

- Does anyone have an answer to prayer you would like to share with the group?

MEMORY VERSE

Do not merely listen to the word, and so deceive yourselves. Do what it says.

James 1:22 (NIV)

Watch the **Video Lesson** now and take notes in your outline. Refer back to the outline during your group discussion.

PROBE IT!

> ***"Sanctify them through thy truth: thy word is truth."***
>
> John 17:17 (KJV)

Bible study without application is dangerous because . . .

- **Knowledge produces ______________________________ .**

> ***Knowledge puffs up, but love builds up.***
>
> 1 Corinthians 8:1 (NIV)

"Puffs up" = inflated with pride that leads to arrogance.

- **Knowledge requires ______________________________ .**

> ***Do not merely listen to the word, and so deceive yourselves. Do what it says.***
>
> James 1:22 (NIV)

> ***I have considered my ways and have turned my steps to your statutes. I will hasten and not delay to obey your commands.***
>
> Psalm 119:59–60 (NIV)

- **Knowledge increases ______________________________ .**

> ***Anyone, then, who knows the good he ought to do and doesn't do it, sins.***
>
> James 4:17 (NIV)

Applying the Bible is difficult because . . .

- **It requires** ____.
- **Satan** ____.
- **We naturally** ____.

Applied Bible study is an act of the will that leads to spiritual maturity. We need to ask the Holy Spirit to give us the strength, determination, and willpower to press through, apply the truth, and make the changes he wants in us.

THE APPLICATION BRIDGE

Ask: **What did it** ______________________? — interpretation

What is the ______________________? — implication

How does it ______________________? — application

The challenge in Bible application is to discover the eternal truths that never change, and then apply them in a world that is always changing.

In your letter you asked me about food offered to idols. All of us know something about this subject. But knowledge makes us proud of ourselves, while love makes us helpful to others. In fact, people who think they know so much don't know anything at all . . . Even though food is offered to idols, we know that none of the idols in this world are alive. After all, there is only one God . . . Not everyone knows these things. In fact, many people have grown up with the belief that idols have life in them. So when they eat meat offered to idols, they are bothered by a weak conscience. But food doesn't bring us any closer to God. We are no worse off if we don't eat, and we are no better off if we do. Don't cause problems for someone with a weak conscience, just because you have the right to eat anything. You know all this, and so it doesn't bother you to eat in the temple of an idol. But suppose a person with a weak conscience sees you and decides to eat food that has been offered to idols. Then what you know has destroyed someone Christ died for. When you sin by hurting a follower with a weak conscience, you sin against Christ. So if I hurt one of the Lord's followers by what I eat, I will never eat meat as long as I live.

1 Corinthians 8:1–13 (CEV)

- **What did it mean then?** Don't eat meat offered to idols if it offends your brother. Even though you know there's nothing wrong with it, it's not the loving thing to do.
- **What is the timeless truth?** Don't allow your freedom to offend your brother. Just because you know something is okay to do doesn't mean you should do it. Even lawful freedom must be used in love. You need to be sensitive to the people around you and to the testimony of your lifestyle.
- **How does it apply now?** Is there anything I am doing out of selfishness, arrogance, or insensitivity that could be causing a brother or sister to stumble? Am I being puffed up by my own knowledge or am I building others up in love?
- **Write it down.** The process isn't finished until you have written down an application of the insights you've discovered through your meditation. Application of God's Word is vitally necessary to our spiritual health and our growth in Christian maturity. If you want to keep your heart soft before God and not let it become hardened, you must diligently, honestly, humbly, and obediently apply his Word to your life.

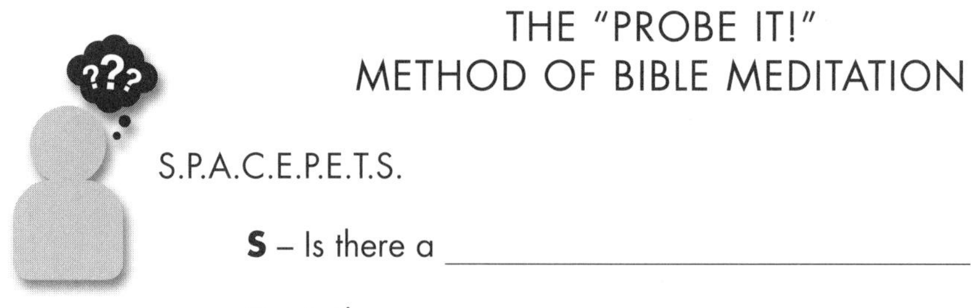

THE "PROBE IT!" METHOD OF BIBLE MEDITATION

S.P.A.C.E.P.E.T.S.

S – Is there a ____________________ to confess?

P – Is there a ____________________ to claim?

A – Is there an ____________________ to change?

C – Is there a ____________________ to obey?

E – Is there an ____________________ to follow?

P – Is there a ____________________ to pray?

E – Is there an ____________________ to avoid?

T – Is there a ____________________ to believe?

S – Is there ____________________ to praise God for?

Notice that every phrase in S.P.A.C.E.P.E.T.S. contains a verb. They are all action-oriented.

DISCOVERY QUESTIONS

- As a group, practice the **Probe It!** method of Bible meditation by applying the S.P.A.C.E.P.E.T.S. questions to Micah 6:8. Write down your thoughts and applications. You might not be able to answer every question. Don't force it. If you can't think of an answer, just move on.

> ***He has shown you, O [man], what is good. And what does the LORD require of you? To act justly and to love mercy and to walk humbly with your God.***
>
> Micah 6:8 (NIV)

S – Is there a sin to confess?

Here's a little help to get you started: How is the church living up to this command in your community? How about your church in particular? What about your personal life: Have you been living in obedience to this verse or are you leaving it up to others?

P – Is there a promise to claim?

What are some of the implied promises and blessings of practicing this verse?

A – Is there an attitude to change?

Apathy, lethargy, thinking the world will take care of itself, leave it to government, etc.

C – Is there a command to obey?

E – Is there an example to follow?

P – Is there a prayer to pray?

E – Is there an error to avoid?

T – Is there a truth to believe?

S – Is there something to praise God for?

How about the privilege of being invited by God to work on his behalf?

PUTTING IT INTO PRACTICE

The Micah 6:8 Assignment

- Now that you have applied the S.P.A.C.E.P.E.T.S. questions to Micah 6:8, are there any changes you need to make in your group project?
- Continue planning your ***Micah 6:8 Assignment***. What details still need to be taken care of?
- Think of a friend who is not currently connected to a church. Why not invite that person to get involved with your group's ***Micah 6:8 Assignment***? What is the worst thing that could happen if you invite them? What is the best thing that could happen if you invite them? Is the potential benefit worth the risk? Tell your group the name of at least one person whom you will invite to participate in your project.

Name

Name

LIVING ON PURPOSE — DISCIPLESHIP

This week in your daily quiet time, read the second half of *The Gospel of Mark*. Using Pastor Rick's S.P.A.C.E.P.E.T.S. questions, practice the **Probe It!** method with the recommended Scripture passages below. Be sure to write down your thoughts and observations about how each passage applies to your life. Use Pastor Rick's Application Bridge principles to help you discover the application. You will find seven **Journal Pages** at the end of this session in your workbook to help you with your devotions.

DAY 15:	Mark 8:34–38	***Jesus teaches about taking up your cross***
DAY 16:	Mark 9:33–35	***Who is the greatest in the kingdom of God?***
DAY 17:	Mark 10:17–31	***Jesus meets the rich young man***
DAY 18:	Mark 11:25	***We must forgive to be forgiven***
DAY 19:	Mark 14:3–9	***A woman anoints Jesus with perfume***
DAY 20:	Mark 15:33–39	***The crucifixion***
DAY 21:	Mark 16:1–20	***The resurrection***

If you miss a day, don't let that discourage you. Just pick up with the current day and keep moving forward. Don't let yesterday's famine rob today of its feast.

PRAYER DIRECTION

- Pray for each other's prayer requests. Use the **Small Group Prayer and Praise Report** on page 196 of this workbook to record prayer requests and answers to prayer.

- Pray about your group's ***Micah 6:8 Assignment***. Pray for the people you will invite to join you. Were there any personal applications from your study of the verse that you need to talk to God about?

- If you prayed with Pastor Rick and opened your heart to Jesus Christ, tell your group so they can pray for you.

GREAT RESOURCES FOR YOUR DEVOTIONAL LIFE

Be sure to visit **www.40daysintheword.com**, where you can:

- Register for Pastor Rick's Daily Hope email devotions. They're free!
- Download the free daily audio devotions for *40 Days in the Word*.
- Learn more about beginning, intermediate, and advanced tools, links, and resources for in-depth Bible study.

S – Is there a sin to confess?

P – Is there a promise to claim?

A – Is there an attitude to change?

C – Is there a command to obey?

E – Is there an example to follow?

P – Is there a prayer to pray?

E – Is there an error to avoid?

T – Is there a truth to believe?

S – Is there something to praise God for?

Probe It!

Jesus teaches about taking up your cross.

Mark 8:34–38

You might not be able to answer every S.P.A.C.E.P.E.T.S. question. Don't force it. If you can't think of an answer, just move on.

Apply It!

How does this passage apply to your life and what will you do about it?

Your prayer . . .

S – Is there a sin to confess?

P – Is there a promise to claim?

A – Is there an attitude to change?

C – Is there a command to obey?

E – Is there an example to follow?

P – Is there a prayer to pray?

E – Is there an error to avoid?

T – Is there a truth to believe?

S – Is there something to praise God for?

Probe It!

Who is the greatest in the Kingdom of God?

Mark 9:33–35

You might not be able to answer every S.P.A.C.E.P.E.T.S. question. Don't force it. If you can't think of an answer, just move on.

Apply It!

How does this passage apply to your life and what will you do about it?

Your prayer . . .

S – Is there a sin to confess?

P – Is there a promise to claim?

A – Is there an attitude to change?

C – Is there a command to obey?

E – Is there an example to follow?

P – Is there a prayer to pray?

E – Is there an error to avoid?

T – Is there a truth to believe?

S – Is there something to praise God for?

Probe It!

Jesus meets the rich young man.

Mark 10:17–31

You might not be able to answer every S.P.A.C.E.P.E.T.S. question. Don't force it. If you can't think of an answer, just move on.

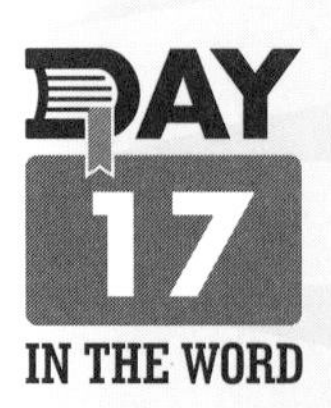

Apply It!

How does this passage apply to your life and what will you do about it?

Your prayer . . .

S – Is there a sin to confess?

P – Is there a promise to claim?

A – Is there an attitude to change?

C – Is there a command to obey?

E – Is there an example to follow?

P – Is there a prayer to pray?

E – Is there an error to avoid?

T – Is there a truth to believe?

S – Is there something to praise God for?

Probe It!

We must forgive to be forgiven.

Mark 11:25

You might not be able to answer every S.P.A.C.E.P.E.T.S. question. Don't force it. If you can't think of an answer, just move on.

Apply It!

How does this passage apply to your life and what will you do about it?

Your prayer . . .

S – Is there a sin to confess?

P – Is there a promise to claim?

A – Is there an attitude to change?

C – Is there a command to obey?

E – Is there an example to follow?

P – Is there a prayer to pray?

E – Is there an error to avoid?

T – Is there a truth to believe?

S – Is there something to praise God for?

Probe It!

A woman anoints Jesus with perfume.

Mark 14:3–9

You might not be able to answer every S.P.A.C.E.P.E.T.S. question. Don't force it. If you can't think of an answer, just move on.

Apply It!

How does this passage apply to your life and what will you do about it?

Your prayer . . .

S – Is there a sin to confess?

P – Is there a promise to claim?

A – Is there an attitude to change?

C – Is there a command to obey?

E – Is there an example to follow?

P – Is there a prayer to pray?

E – Is there an error to avoid?

T – Is there a truth to believe?

S – Is there something to praise God for?

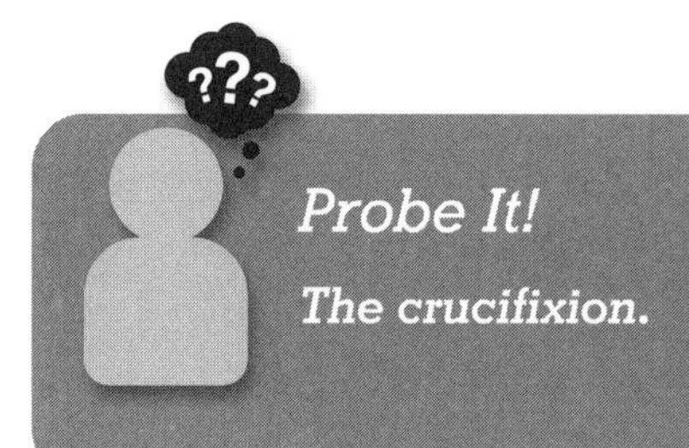

Probe It!

The crucifixion.

Mark 15:33–39

You might not be able to answer every S.P.A.C.E.P.E.T.S. question. Don't force it. If you can't think of an answer, just move on.

Apply It!

How does this passage apply to your life and what will you do about it?

Your prayer . . .

S – Is there a sin to confess?

P – Is there a promise to claim?

A – Is there an attitude to change?

C – Is there a command to obey?

E – Is there an example to follow?

P – Is there a prayer to pray?

E – Is there an error to avoid?

T – Is there a truth to believe?

S – Is there something to praise God for?

You might not be able to answer every S.P.A.C.E.P.E.T.S. question. Don't force it. If you can't think of an answer, just move on.

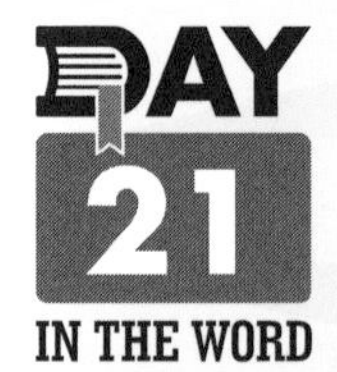

Apply It!

How does this passage apply to your life and what will you do about it?

Your prayer . . .

Session Four
PARAPHRASE IT!

CATCHING UP

- How are you doing in your daily quiet time? Are you feeling encouraged or discouraged?

- Would anyone like to share an insight you discovered in *The Gospel of Mark* by using S.P.A.C.E.P.E.T.S. this past week?

MEMORY VERSE

I have hidden your word in my heart that I might not sin against you.

Psalm 119:11 (NIV)

Watch the **Video Lesson** now and take notes in your outline. Refer back to the outline during your group discussion.

PARAPHRASE IT!

FOUR COMMON PROBLEMS IN A DAILY QUIET TIME

1. The problem of ______________________ . . .

   The Battle of the ______________________

   What to do . . .

   Go to bed ______________________ .

   Get up ______________________ .

   Be aware of ______________________ .

   Go to bed with ______________________ on your mind.

> ***Blessed is the man . . . who delight[s] in the law of the Lord, and on his law he meditates day and night.***
>
> Psalm 1:1–2 (NIV)

2. The problem of ______________________ . . .

   The Battle of the ______________________

   Common Causes of Spiritual Dry Spells:

   ____

   Your ______________________ condition

   Trying to ______________________ in a hurry

   Being in a ______________________

   Not sharing your ______________________ with others

> ***Let us not become weary in doing good, for at the proper time we will reap a harvest if we do not give up.***
>
> Galatians 6:9 (NIV)

3. **The problem of ______________________ . . .**

   The Battle of the ______________________

   What to do . . .

   Be sure you are thoroughly ______________________ .

   Read and pray ______________________ .

   ______________________ while praying.

   Keep a ______________________ handy.

4. **The problem of ______________________ . . .**

   The Battle of ______________________

   What to do . . .

   Make a ______________________ with God.

   Put it into your ______________________ .

   Be prepared for the devil's ______________________ and ______________________ .

   Leave your Bible ______________________ .

   Rely on the ______________________ .

THE "PARAPHRASE IT!" METHOD OF BIBLE MEDITATION

- Read the verse or passage over and over.
- Think about what God is saying to you.
- Put it into your own words.
- Search your heart to see how the verse applies to you.
- Talk to God about it.

Ultimately, you want to be able to explain the entire verse or passage in your own words. It's not enough just to know what the Bible says; you also need to know what the Bible means. If you can't put it in your own words, then you don't truly understand what it is saying.

I have hidden your word in my heart that I might not sin against you.

Psalm 119:11 (NIV)

Pastor Rick's paraphrase: "I have memorized your Word, Lord, so I won't give in to temptation."

Think of it as two parts of a conversation. Say back to God what you heard him say to you, but use your own words. Then respond to him with your thoughts and prayers, based on the passage you just read.

DISCOVERY QUESTIONS

- As a group, practice the **Paraphrase It!** method of Bible meditation using Hebrews 4:12 (NIV).

> ***For the word of God is living and active. Sharper than any double-edged sword, it penetrates even to dividing soul and spirit, joints and marrow; it judges the thoughts and attitudes of the heart.***
>
> Hebrews 4:12 (NIV)

- Read the verse several times. What is God saying to you in this passage?

____

____

____

____

- Put it into your own words.

____

____

____

____

- How does this verse apply to you, and what will you do about it? How willing are you to let the Word of God do its work in you? Is this something you fear or look forward to?

____

____

____

____

____

____

____

PUTTING IT INTO PRACTICE

The Micah 6:8 Assignment

- As a group, practice the **Paraphrase It!** method on Micah 6:8. What is God saying to you in this passage? Put it into your own words.

> ***He has shown you, O [man], what is good. And what does the LORD require of you? To act justly and to love mercy and to walk humbly with your God.***
>
> Micah 6:8 (NIV)

____

____

____

____

- What remaining details and loose ends need to be taken care of in the preparation phase of your ***Micah 6:8 Assignment***? Take a few minutes to discuss your plans.

LIVING ON PURPOSE

This week in your daily quiet time, read *The Book of James*. It's only five chapters long. There is no need to rush your way through the book. Remember, it's not how much of the Bible you get through every day; it's how deeply the Bible gets through to you. So take your time.

Practice the **Paraphrase It!** method using the seven suggested passages below. Be sure to write down your thoughts and observations about how each passage applies to your life. You will find seven **Journal Pages** at the end of this session in your workbook to help you with your devotions.

> **DAY 22:** ***Consider it pure joy, my brothers, whenever you face trials of many kinds, because you know that the testing of your faith develops perseverance. Perseverance must finish its work so that you may be mature and complete, not lacking anything.***
>
> James 1:2–4 (NIV)

DAY 23: *My dear brothers, take note of this: Everyone should be quick to listen, slow to speak and slow to become angry, for man's anger does not bring about the righteous life that God desires.*

James 1:19–20 (NIV)

DAY 24: *Do not merely listen to the word, and so deceive yourselves. Do what it says. Anyone who listens to the word but does not do what it says is like a man who looks at his face in a mirror and, after looking at himself, goes away and immediately forgets what he looks like. But the man who looks intently into the perfect law that gives freedom, and continues to do this, not forgetting what he has heard, but doing it—he will be blessed in what he does.*

James 1:22–25 (NIV)

DAY 25: *In the same way, faith by itself, if it is not accompanied by action, is dead. But someone will say, "You have faith; I have deeds." Show me your faith without deeds, and I will show you my faith by what I do.*

James 2:17–18 (NIV)

DAY 26: *Who is wise and understanding among you? Let him show it by his good life, by deeds done in the humility that comes from wisdom.*

James 3:13 (NIV)

DAY 27: *Humble yourselves before the Lord, and he will lift you up.*

James 4:10 (NIV)

DAY 28: *My brothers, if one of you should wander from the truth and someone should bring him back, remember this: Whoever turns a sinner from the error of his way will save him from death and cover over a multitude of sins.*

James 5:19–20 (NIV)

If you miss a day, don't let that discourage you. Just pick up with the current day and keep moving forward. Don't let yesterday's famine rob today of its feast.

PRAYER DIRECTION

- If you're struggling in your daily quiet time, ask your group to pray for you.
- Pray for each other's prayer requests. Use the **Small Group Prayer and Praise Report** on page 196 of the workbook to record prayer requests and answers to prayer.
- Pray about your group's ***Micah 6:8 Assignment***.

DIVING DEEPER

If you want to go deeper in your personal Bible study this week, read the bonus chapter titled **The Chapter Summary Method of Bible Study** on page 143 of this workbook. In this chapter, Pastor Rick teaches you to read a chapter of the Bible at least five times, then write down a summary of the central thoughts you find in it. We suggest you practice this method on James chapter 1 this week.

GREAT RESOURCES FOR YOUR DEVOTIONAL LIFE

Be sure to visit **www.40daysintheword.com**, where you can:

- Register for Pastor Rick's Daily Hope email devotions. They're free!
- Download the free daily audio devotions for *40 Days in the Word*.
- Learn more about beginning, intermediate, and advanced tools, links, and resources for in-depth Bible study.

Paraphrase It!

Consider it pure joy, my brothers, whenever you face trials of many kinds, because you know that the testing of your faith develops perseverance. Perseverance must finish its work so that you may be mature and complete, not lacking anything.

James 1:2–4 (NIV)

Read the passage several times. Then put it into your own words.

Apply It!

How does this passage apply to your life and what will you do about it?

Your prayer . . .

Paraphrase It!

My dear brothers, take note of this: Everyone should be quick to listen, slow to speak and slow to become angry, for man's anger does not bring about the righteous life that God desires.

James 1:19–20 (NIV)

Read the passage several times. Then put it into your own words.

Apply It!

How does this passage apply to your life and what will you do about it?

Your prayer . . .

Paraphrase It!

Do not merely listen to the word, and so deceive yourselves. Do what it says. Anyone who listens to the word but does not do what it says is like a man who looks at his face in a mirror and, after looking at himself, goes away and immediately forgets what he looks like. But the man who looks intently into the perfect law that gives freedom, and continues to do this, not forgetting what he has heard, but doing it—he will be blessed in what he does.

James 1:22–25 (NIV)

Read the passage several times. Then put it into your own words.

DAY 24 IN THE WORD

Apply It!

How does this passage apply to your life and what will you do about it?

Your prayer . . .

Paraphrase It!

In the same way, faith by itself, if it is not accompanied by action, is dead. But someone will say, "You have faith; I have deeds." Show me your faith without deeds, and I will show you my faith by what I do.

James 2:17–18 (NIV)

Read the passage several times. Then put it into your own words.

DAY 25 IN THE WORD

Apply It!

How does this passage apply to your life and what will you do about it?

Your prayer . . .

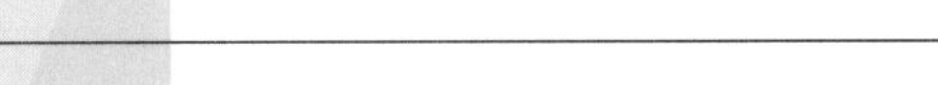

Paraphrase It!

Who is wise and understanding among you? Let him show it by his good life, by deeds done in the humility that comes from wisdom.

James 3:13 (NIV)

Read the passage several times. Then put it into your own words.

Apply It!

How does this passage apply to your life and what will you do about it?

Your prayer . . .

DAY 26 IN THE WORD

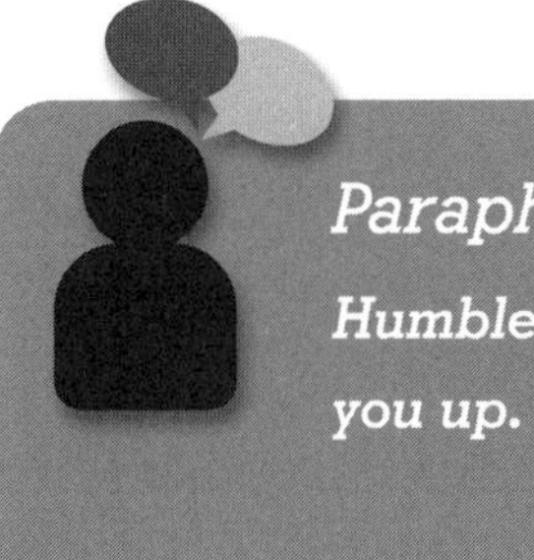

Paraphrase It!

Humble yourselves before the Lord, and he will lift you up.

James 4:10 (NIV)

Read the passage several times. Then put it into your own words.

Apply It!

How does this passage apply to your life and what will you do about it?

Your prayer . . .

Paraphrase It!

My brothers, if one of you should wander from the truth and someone should bring him back, remember this: Whoever turns a sinner from the error of his way will save him from death and cover over a multitude of sins.

James 5:19–20 (NIV)

Read the passage several times. Then put it into your own words.

DAY 28 IN THE WORD

Apply It!

How does this passage apply to your life and what will you do about it?

Your prayer . . .

Session Five
PERSONALIZE IT! PRAY IT!

CATCHING UP

- Describe a time when it seemed as though God spoke directly to you in the Bible.

- Do you have a favorite Bible verse or story? If so, what is it?

MEMORY VERSE

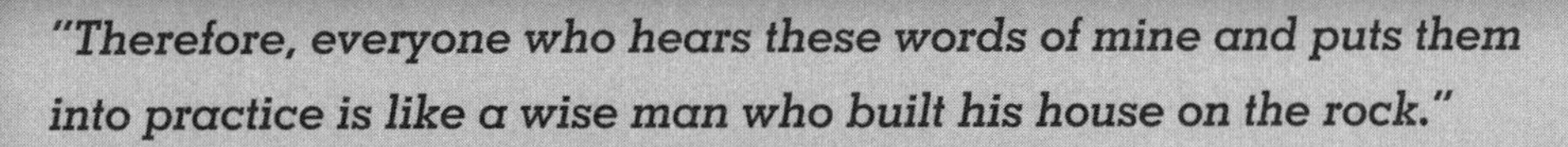

"Therefore, everyone who hears these words of mine and puts them into practice is like a wise man who built his house on the rock."

Matthew 7:24 (NIV)

Watch the **Video Lesson** now and take notes in your outline. Refer back to the outline during your group discussion.

PERSONALIZE IT! PRAY IT!

> ***Guard my words as your most precious possession. Write them down, and also keep them deep within your heart.***
>
> Proverbs 7:2–3 (TLB)

> ***The law you gave means more to me than all the money in the world.***
>
> Psalm 119:72 (GNT)

BENEFITS OF MEMORIZING SCRIPTURE

- **Memorizing Scripture helps me ________________________________ ________________________________.**

  In order to say, "It is written," we first have to know *what* is written.

> ***I have hidden your word in my heart [so] that I might not sin against you.***
>
> Psalm 119:11 (NIV)

- **Memorizing Scripture helps me make ______________________________ ________________________.**

> ***Your word is a lamp to guide my feet and a light for my path.***
>
> Psalm 119:105 (NLT)

The more you know what God says, the more you will know how God thinks.

- **Memorizing Scripture ______________________________ when I'm under stress.**

> ***Your promises to me . . . are my only hope. They give me strength in all my troubles; how they refresh and revive me!***
>
> Psalm 119:49–50 (TLB)

- **Memorizing Scripture __________________________________ when I'm sad.**

> ***Your words . . . sustain me . . . They bring joy to my sorrowing heart and delight me.***
>
> Jeremiah 15:16 (TLB)

- **Memorizing Scripture helps me __________________________ _________________________________.**

> ***Always be prepared to give an answer to everyone who asks you to give the reason for the hope that you have. But do [it] with gentleness and respect.***
>
> 1 Peter 3:15 (NIV)

HOW TO MEMORIZE SCRIPTURE

1. Pick a ______________________ .

> *"Therefore, everyone who hears these words of mine and puts them into practice is like a wise man who built his house on the rock."*
>
> Matthew 7:24 (NIV)

2. Say the ______________________ before and after the verse.
3. Read the verse ______________________ many times.
4. Break the verse into ______________________ .

> Matthew 7:24
>
> *"Therefore / everyone who hears these words of mine / and puts them into practice / is like a wise man / who built his house on the rock."*
>
> Matthew 7:24

5. Emphasize ______________________ in each phrase.

> Matthew 7:24
>
> *"Therefore / everyone who **hears** these words of mine / and puts them into **practice** / is like a **wise** man / who built his house on the **rock**."*
>
> Matthew 7:24

6. Always memorize the verse ______________________ .

THE "PERSONALIZE IT!" METHOD OF BIBLE MEDITATION

Put your name in place of the pronouns or nouns used in Scripture. For example . . .

For God so loved (________________) that he gave his one and only Son, that if (________________) believes in him, (________________) shall not perish but have eternal life.

John 3:16

He who began a good work in (________________________) will carry it on to completion until the day of Jesus Christ.

Philippians 1:6

Rewrite the verse in the first person, as though God were saying it directly to you, like this . . .

"I began a good work in you, (________________________), and I will carry it on to completion."

Philippians 1:6

"Trust in me, (______________), with all your heart and do not lean on your own understanding. In all your ways acknowledge me, and I will direct your paths."

Proverbs 3:5–6

"I am your Shepherd, (________________), you shall not be in want. I make you lie down in green pastures, I lead you beside quiet waters, I restore your soul. I guide you, (______________), in the paths of righteousness for my name's sake."

Psalm 23:1–3

The Word of God is his love letter to you. And he wants you to open it and experience the joy of getting to know him through his Word. That's what devotional reading is all about. Not just knowing the Word, but getting to know the Author personally.

THE "PRAY IT!" METHOD OF BIBLE MEDITATION

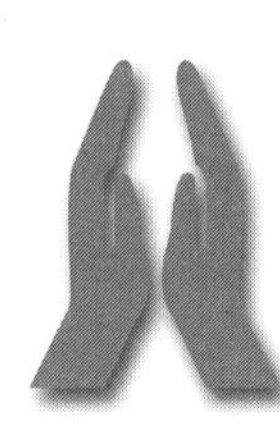

Put the passage you are studying into the first person singular form from you, turn it into a prayer, and pray it back to God.

Thank you, Lord, for being my Shepherd, and that I lack nothing. Thank you for making me lie down in green pastures, and for leading me beside the quiet waters. Thank you for restoring my soul. Thank you for guiding me in the paths of righteousness for your name's sake.

Psalm 23:1–3

Help me, Lord, to trust you with all of my heart and to stop leaning on my own understanding. Please give me the faith to acknowledge you in all my ways so that you can direct my paths.

Proverbs 3:5–6

Then write down your thoughts and prayers. And always, ***always***, find the application to your life. Look for the timeless truth in the verse. Ask yourself: How do I look in the mirror of this passage? What am I seeing in the light of this truth? How does the verse or passage apply to my life right now? What does God want me to do about it? How can I put it into practice? What do I need to think or feel differently about? What is God asking me to do or stop doing, to believe or stop believing? How does he want me to live from now on?

Four Factors in Writing a Good Application

Your application should be . . .

________________________**—write it in the first person**

________________________**—something specific you can do**

________________________**—something you know you can accomplish**

________________________**—measurable so you'll know when you have done it; set a deadline**

For example . . .

> ***All man's efforts are for his mouth, yet his appetite is never satisfied.***
>
> Ecclesiastes 6:7 (NIV)

Personal: "I need to . . ."

Practical: "I need to lose some weight."

Possible: "I need to lose 10 pounds."

Provable: "I need to lose 10 pounds before the end of the month."

DISCOVERY QUESTIONS

- As a group, practice the **Personalize It!** method using 1 Corinthians 6:19–20. (We'll practice the **Pray It!** method during our prayer time.) Insert your name into the passage and rewrite it as though God were saying it directly to you.

> ***Do you not know that your body is a temple of the Holy Spirit, who is in you, whom you have received from God? You are not your own; you were bought at a price. Therefore honor God with your body.***
>
> 1 Corinthians 6:19–20 (NIV)

- What does it mean to you that your body is a temple of the Holy Spirit? Why do you think God wants to live in you through his Spirit?

- In light of this truth, how do you think God wants you to live? Review Pastor Rick's four points of application. How can you honor God by treating your body as a temple of the Holy Spirit in a personal, practical, possible, and provable way?

PUTTING IT INTO PRACTICE

- Practice the **Personalize It!** method on Micah 6:8 by inserting your name in the verse, and rewriting it as though God were saying it directly to you.

> ***He has shown you, O [man], what is good. And what does the LORD require of you? To act justly and to love mercy and to walk humbly with your God.***
>
> Micah 6:8 (NIV)

- There are just two weeks remaining in *40 Days in the Word*. It would be great if your group completed your ***Micah 6:8 Assignment*** before this series ends. Is anything standing in the way?

- We would love to hear about your project! Ask your group's ***Micah 6:8 Assignment*** champion to go to **www.40daysintheword.com** and click on ***The Micah 6:8 Assignment*** link to share your story and photos.

LIVING ON PURPOSE

This week, let's read *The Book of Philippians* again. Read it with fresh eyes and "ears" to hear what God has to say to you. During your daily quiet time, use the **Personalize It!** method on each of the verses below by inserting your name in place of the nouns or pronouns and rewriting the verse as though God were saying it directly to you. Be sure to write down your thoughts and observations about how each passage applies to your life. Then pray the verse back to God. You will find seven **Journal Pages** at the end of this session in your workbook to help you with your devotions.

DAY 29: *Being confident of this, that he who began a good work in you will carry it on to completion until the day of Christ Jesus.*

Philippians 1:6 (NIV)

DAY 30: *Whatever happens, conduct yourselves in a manner worthy of the gospel of Christ.*

Philippians 1:27 (NIV)

DAY 31: *For God is working in you, giving you the desire and the power to do what pleases him.*

Philippians 2:13 (NLT)

DAY 32: *I press on to take hold of that for which Christ Jesus took hold of me.*

Philippians 3:12 (BSB)

DAY 33: *Do not be anxious about anything, but in everything, by prayer and petition, with thanksgiving, present your requests to God. And the peace of God, which transcends all understanding, will guard your hearts and your minds in Christ Jesus.*

Philippians 4:6–7 (NIV)

DAY 34: ***I can do all things through Christ who strengthens me.***

Philippians 4:13 (NKJV)

DAY 35: ***My God will meet all your needs according to his glorious riches in Christ Jesus.***

Philippians 4:19 (NIV)

If you miss a day, don't let that discourage you. Just pick up with the current day and keep moving forward. Don't let yesterday's famine rob today of its feast.

PRAYER DIRECTION

- During your group prayer time, practice the **Pray It!** method by praying the Scripture verses in the **Living on Purpose** section as blessings over each other.
- Pray for each other's prayer requests. Use the **Small Group Prayer and Praise Report** on page 196 of this workbook to record prayer requests and answers to prayer.
- Pray about your group's ***Micah 6:8 Assignment***.

DIVING DEEPER

If you want to go deeper in your personal Bible study this week, review the list of **Twenty Verses Every Believer Needs to Memorize** on page 114 of this workbook. Select one or two verses that you will memorize this week.

GREAT RESOURCES FOR YOUR DEVOTIONAL LIFE

Be sure to visit **www.40daysintheword.com**, where you can:

- Register for Pastor Rick's Daily Hope email devotions. They're free!
- Download the free daily audio devotions for *40 Days in the Word*.
- Learn more about beginning, intermediate, and advanced tools, links, and resources for in-depth Bible study.

Personalize It! Pray It!

Being confident of this, that he who began a good work in you will carry it on to completion until the day of Christ Jesus.

Philippians 1:6 (NIV)

Insert your name in place of the nouns or pronouns and rewrite the verse as though God were saying it directly to you.

Apply It!

How does this passage apply to your life and what will you do about it?

Pray It!

Pray Philippians 1:6 back to God.

DAY 29 IN THE WORD

Personalize It! Pray It!

Whatever happens, conduct yourselves in a manner worthy of the gospel of Christ.

Philippians 1:27 (NIV)

Insert your name in place of the nouns or pronouns and rewrite the verse as though God were saying it directly to you.

Apply It!

How does this passage apply to your life and what will you do about it?

Pray It!

Pray Philippians 1:27 back to God.

Personalize It! Pray It!

For God is working in you, giving you the desire and the power to do what pleases him.

Philippians 2:13 (NLT)

Insert your name in place of the nouns or pronouns and rewrite the verse as though God were saying it directly to you.

Apply It!

How does this passage apply to your life and what will you do about it?

Pray It!

Pray Philippians 2:13 back to God.

Personalize It! Pray It!

I press on to take hold of that for which Christ Jesus took hold of me.

Philippians 3:12 (BSB)

Insert your name in place of the nouns or pronouns and rewrite the verse as though God were saying it directly to you.

Apply It!

How does this passage apply to your life and what will you do about it?

Pray It!

Pray Philippians 3:12 back to God.

Personalize It! Pray It!

Do not be anxious about anything, but in everything, by prayer and petition, with thanksgiving, present your requests to God. And the peace of God, which transcends all understanding, will guard your hearts and your minds in Christ Jesus.

Philippians 4:6–7 (NIV)

Insert your name in place of the nouns or pronouns and rewrite the passage as though God were saying it directly to you.

Apply It!

How does this passage apply to your life and what will you do about it?

Pray It!

Pray Philippians 4:6–7 back to God.

Personalize It! Pray It!

I can do all things through Christ who strengthens me.

Philippians 4:13 (NKJV)

Insert your name in place of the nouns or pronouns and rewrite the verse as though God were saying it directly to you.

Apply It!

How does this passage apply to your life and what will you do about it?

Pray It!

Pray Philippians 4:13 back to God.

Personalize It! Pray It!

My God will meet all your needs according to his glorious riches in Christ Jesus.

Philippians 4:19 (NIV)

Insert your name in place of the nouns or pronouns and rewrite the verse as though God were saying it directly to you.

Apply It!

How does this passage apply to your life and what will you do about it?

Pray It!

Pray Philippians 4:19 back to God.

Session Six
PRINCIPLES OF BIBLE INTERPRETATION

CATCHING UP

- Which of the six methods of devotional Bible study have you found to be the most helpful?

- How has your daily quiet time improved during *40 Days in the Word*?

MEMORY VERSE

Your word is a lamp to my feet and a light for my path.

Psalm 119:105 (NIV)

Watch the **Video Lesson** now and take notes in your outline. Refer back to the outline during your group discussion.

PRINCIPLES OF BIBLE INTERPRETATION

"If you continue in my word you are my disciples indeed. And you shall know the truth and the truth shall make you free."

John 8:31–32 (MKJV)

HOW TO CONTINUE IN THE WORD

- **Make a ______________________________.**

Decide that you are going to commit to this habit.

If you wait for perfect conditions, you will never get anything done.

Ecclesiastes 11:4 (TLB)

- **Make a ______________________________.**

Announce your intentions, and give your family or friends permission to check up on you.

- **Make a ______________________________.**

Don't allow any exceptions to knock you off track.

- **______________________________.**

Get a spiritual partner for support and encouragement.

Two are better off than one, because together they can work more effectively. If one of them falls down, the other can help him up.

Ecclesiastes 4:9–10 (GNT)

- **____________________ on God.**

Rely on God's power to help you establish the habit of a daily quiet time.

> ***For the Spirit God has given us . . . fills us with power, love, and self-control.***
>
> 2 Timothy 1:7 (GNT)

God has something to say to you every day through his Word, and he wants to hear what you have to say every day in prayer. Don't deny God or yourself the pleasure and the privilege of friendship with him.

BASIC PRINCIPLES OF BIBLE INTERPRETATION

- **____________________ and the ____________________ are necessary for proper interpretation.**

The Bible is a spiritual book that can only be truly understood by people who are spiritually alive through Jesus Christ.

> ***No one knows the thoughts of God except the Spirit of God. We have not received the spirit of the world but the Spirit who is from God, [so] that we may understand what God has freely given us . . . The man without the Spirit does not accept the things that come from the Spirit of God, for they are foolishness to him, and he cannot understand them, because they are spiritually discerned . . . But we have the mind of Christ.***
>
> 1 Corinthians 2:11–16 (NIV)

In other words, to make sense of what the Bible says and means, you have to have a personal relationship with the Author.

> ***"But when he, the Spirit of truth, comes, he will guide you into all truth . . . He will bring glory to me by taking from what is mine and making it known to you."***
>
> John 16:13–14 (NIV)

- **The ____________________ is its own best ____________________ .**

Scripture best explains and interprets Scripture. By looking up other verses on the same topic, you will get a much bigger and clearer picture of what God has to say about it.

- **Read the ____ with the ______________________________________ in mind, and read the ____ with the ____ in mind.**

- **Always interpret ______________________________ passages in the light of ______________________________ passages.**

Since the Bible is its own best commentary, you need to look at the full council of God in Scripture to get a clear understanding of unclear passages.

> ***If it is true, as some claim, that the dead are not raised to life, why are those people being baptized for the dead?***
>
> 1 Corinthians 15:29 (GNT)

- **Don't form a ______________________________ based solely on a ______________________________.**

> ***Very early in the morning, while it was still dark, Jesus got up, left the house and went off to a solitary place, where he prayed.***
>
> Mark 1:35 (NIV)

You cannot turn the story of when Jesus prayed into a command or a doctrine about when to have your quiet time.

- **Don't interpret ______________________ based on ______________________; instead, interpret ______________________ based on ______________________.**

Exegesis = to draw out of the text the truth that God put there.

Eisegesis = to read into the text some idea or theory that you want to see there.

When you study the Bible, you're not trying to get God to agree with your ideas about something, or to convince him that your position is right. You have to come with an open heart and invite God to conform you to his will by showing you the truth that is in his Word. Remember, he's God and you're not.

DISCOVERY QUESTIONS

As a group, review the six methods of biblical meditation using this week's **Memory Verse:**

> *Your word is a lamp to my feet and a light for my path.*
>
> Psalm 119:105 (NIV)

- **Pronounce It!** Which word stands out most prominently to you?

- **Picture It!** What do the phrases "lamp to my feet" and "light for my path" look like to you?

- **Probe It!** Use the S.P.A.C.E.P.E.T.S. questions from Session Three.

- **Paraphrase It!** Put it into your own words. Can you think of other metaphors to use?

- **Personalize It!** Insert your name in place of the first-person pronouns; then rewrite it again, as though God were saying it directly to you.

- **Pray It!** Take a moment and pray this verse back to God, thanking him for the direction, wisdom, strength, and comfort you find in his Word.

PUTTING IT INTO PRACTICE

The Micah 6:8 Assignment

- We pray your ***Micah 6:8 Assignment*** will be the starting point of a lifestyle of service for your group and for you as an individual. Our hope is that you will look back after these 40 days and not say, "Look at what we did," but rather, "Look at what we started!" What can your group do to continue reaching out to your community with the love of Jesus Christ?

- Pastor Rick would love to hear about your small group's ***Micah 6:8 Assignment***. Go to **www.40daysintheword.com** and click on ***The Micah 6:8 Assignment*** link. You will be able to share your group's story and post photos for other *40 Days in the Word* groups to see. Thanks!

LIVING ON PURPOSE

During your daily quiet time this week, use Psalm 1 every day to review all six methods of Bible meditation. Remember to use Pastor Rick's Application Bridge questions (see Session Three) to discover how the psalm applies to your life. Be sure to write down your thoughts, observations, and applications. You will find five **Journal Pages** at the end of this session in your workbook to help you with your devotions.

DAY 36: Choose a verse from Psalm 1 to Pronounce (see Session One).

DAY 37: Picture the imagery in Psalm 1 (see Session Two).

DAY 38: Probe Psalm 1 with S.P.A.C.E.P.E.T.S. questions (see Session Three).

DAY 39: Paraphrase the entire psalm in your own words (see Session Four).

DAY 40: Personalize all of Psalm 1 as though God were saying it to you. Then pray it back to God (see Session Five).

If you miss a day, don't let that discourage you. Just pick up with the current day and keep moving forward. Don't let yesterday's famine rob today of its feast.

PRAYER DIRECTION

- Before you pray for each other's requests, spend a few minutes offering prayers of thanks for what God has done in your life during *40 Days in the Word*.
- Pray for each other's prayer requests. Use the **Small Group Prayer and Praise Report** on page 196 of this workbook to record prayer requests and answers to prayer.
- Pray about your group's ***Micah 6:8 Assignment***.

DIVING DEEPER

If you want to go deeper in your personal Bible study this week, read the bonus chapter titled **The Character Quality Method of Bible Study** on page 153 of this workbook. In this chapter, Pastor Rick teaches you how to choose a character quality you would like to work on in your life and study what the Bible says about it. You will need some additional study tools to complete this method of Bible study. You can read about them in the article, **Tools for Effective Bible Study** on page 170 of your workbook.

GREAT RESOURCES FOR YOUR DEVOTIONAL LIFE

Be sure to visit **www.40daysintheword.com**, where you can:

- Register for Pastor Rick's Daily Hope email devotions. They're free!
- Download the free daily audio devotions for *40 Days in the Word*.
- Learn more about beginning, intermediate, and advanced tools, links, and resources for in-depth Bible study.

Select a verse from Psalm 1. Read the entire verse several times, stopping after each word to write down your thoughts.

Apply It!

How does this verse apply to your life and what will you do about it?

Your prayer . . .

Picture It!

Psalm 1:1–6

Picture the imagery of the psalm.

Apply It!

How does this passage apply to your life and what will you do about it?

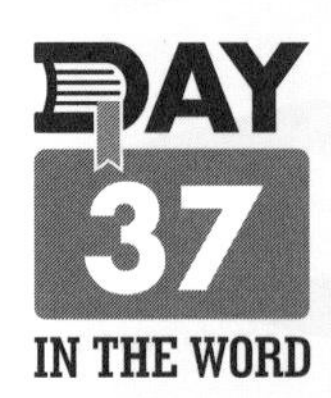

Your prayer . . .

You might not be able to answer every question. Don't force it. If you can't think of an answer, just move on.

S – Is there a sin to confess?

P – Is there a promise to claim?

A – Is there an attitude to change?

C – Is there a command to obey?

E – Is there an example to follow?

P – Is there a prayer to pray?

E – Is there an error to avoid?

T – Is there a truth to believe?

S – Is there something to praise God for?

Apply It!

How does this passage apply to your life and what will you do about it?

Your prayer . . .

Paraphrase It!

Psalm 1:1–6

Read the passage several times. Then put it into your own words.

Apply It!

How does this passage apply to your life and what will you do about it?

Your prayer . . .

Personalize It!

Psalm 1:1–6

Insert your name in place of the nouns or pronouns and rewrite the psalm as though God were saying it directly to you.

Apply It!

How does this passage apply to your life and what will you do about it?

Pray It!

Pray Psalm 1 back to God.

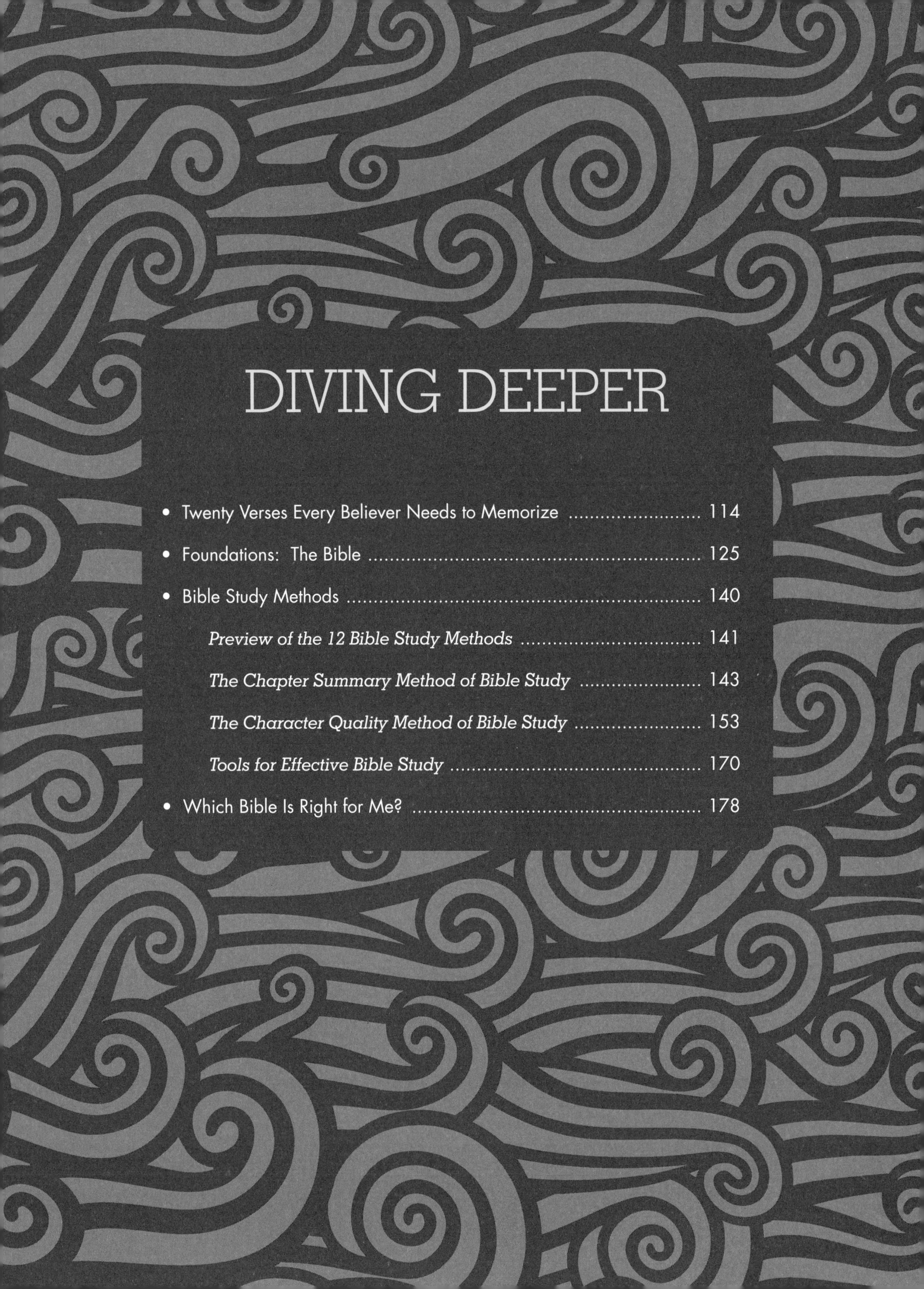

DIVING DEEPER

Twenty Verses Every Believer Needs to Memorize

"For God so loved the world that He gave His only begotten Son, that whoever believes in Him should not perish but have everlasting life." (John 3:16 NKJV)

If we confess our sins, he is faithful and just and will forgive us our sins and purify us from all unrighteousness. **(1 John 1:9 NIV)**

For the wages of sin is death; but the gift of God is eternal life through Jesus Christ our Lord. (Romans 6:23 KJV)

For it is by grace you have been saved, through faith—and this not from yourselves, it is the gift of God—not by works, so that no one can boast. **(Ephesians 2:8–9 NIV)**

I have been crucified with Christ and I no longer live, but Christ lives in me. The life I live in the body, I live by faith in the Son of God, who loved me and gave himself for me. (Galatians 2:20 NIV)

Anyone who belongs to Christ has become a new person. The old life is gone; a new life has begun! **(2 Corinthians 5:17 NLT)**

Being confident of this, that he who began a good work in you will carry it on to completion until the day of Christ Jesus. (Philippians 1:6 NIV)

I can do all things through Christ who strengthens me. **(Philippians 4:13 NKJV)**

"Therefore go and make disciples of all nations, baptizing them in the name of the Father and of the Son and of the Holy Spirit, and teaching them to obey everything I have commanded you. And surely I am with you always, to the very end of the age." (Matthew 28:19–20 NIV)

"'Love the Lord your God with all your heart and with all your soul and with all your strength and with all your mind'; and, 'Love your neighbor as yourself.'" **(Luke 10:27 NIV)**

"I am the way and the truth and the life. No one comes to the Father except through me." (John 14:6 NIV)

"I am the vine; you are the branches. If a man remains in me and I in him, he will bear much fruit; apart from me you can do nothing." **(John 15:5 NIV)**

"Come to me, all you who are weary and burdened, and I will give you rest." (Matthew 11:28 NIV)

You will keep him in perfect peace, whose mind is stayed on You, because he trusts in You. **(Isaiah 26:3 NKJV)**

Cast all your anxiety on him because he cares for you. (1 Peter 5:7 NIV)

Do not be anxious about anything, but in everything, by prayer and petition, with thanksgiving, present your requests to God. And the peace of God, which transcends all understanding, will guard your hearts and your minds in Christ Jesus. **(Philippians 4:6–7 NIV)**

"Fear not, for I am with you; be not dismayed, for I am your God. I will strengthen you, yes, I will help you, I will uphold you with My righteous right hand." (Isaiah 41:10 NKJV)

"But seek first the kingdom of God and His righteousness, and all these things shall be added to you." **(Matthew 6:33 NKJV)**

Trust in the LORD with all your heart, and lean not on your own understanding; in all your ways acknowledge Him, and He shall direct your paths. (Proverbs 3:5–6 NKJV)

Your word is a lamp to my feet and a light for my path. **(Psalm 119:105 NIV)**

"For God so loved the world that He gave His only begotten Son, that whoever believes in Him should not perish but have everlasting life."

John 3:16 NKJV

If we confess our sins, he is faithful and just and will forgive us our sins and purify us from all unrighteousness.

1 John 1:9 NIV

For the wages of sin is death; but the gift of God is eternal life through Jesus Christ our Lord.

Romans 6:23 KJV

For it is by grace you have been saved, through faith—and this not from yourselves, it is the gift of God—not by works, so that no one can boast.

Ephesians 2:8–9 NIV

I have been crucified with Christ and I no longer live, but Christ lives in me. The life I live in the body, I live by faith in the Son of God, who loved me and gave himself for me.

Galatians 2:20 NIV

Anyone who belongs to Christ has become a new person. The old life is gone; a new life has begun!

2 Corinthians 5:17 NLT

Being confident of this, that he who began a good work in you will carry it on to completion until the day of Christ Jesus.

Philippians 1:6 NIV

I can do all things through Christ who strengthens me.

Philippians 4:13 NKJV

"Therefore go and make disciples of all nations, baptizing them in the name of the Father and of the Son and of the Holy Spirit, and teaching them to obey everything I have commanded you. And surely I am with you always, to the very end of the age."

Matthew 28:19–20 NIV

"'Love the Lord your God with all your heart and with all your soul and with all your strength and with all your mind'; and, 'Love your neighbor as yourself.'"

Luke 10:27 NIV

"I am the way and the truth and the life. No one comes to the Father except through me."

John 14:6 NIV

"I am the vine; you are the branches. If a man remains in me and I in him, he will bear much fruit; apart from me you can do nothing."

John 15:5 NIV

*"Come to me,
all you who are weary and
burdened, and I will give
you rest."*

Matthew 11:28 NIV

*You will keep him in
perfect peace, whose mind
is stayed on You, because
he trusts in You.*

Isaiah 26:3 NKJV

*Cast all your
anxiety on him because he
cares for you.*

1 Peter 5:7 NIV

*Do not be anxious
about anything, but in
everything, by prayer
and petition, with
thanksgiving, present
your requests to God.
And the peace of God,
which transcends all
understanding, will guard
your hearts and your
minds in Christ Jesus.*

Philippians 4:6–7 NIV

"Fear not, for I am with you; be not dismayed, for I am your God. I will strengthen you, yes, I will help you, I will uphold you with My righteous right hand."

Isaiah 41:10 NKJV

"But seek first the kingdom of God and His righteousness, and all these things shall be added to you."

Matthew 6:33 NKJV

Trust in the LORD with all your heart, and lean not on your own understanding; in all your ways acknowledge Him, and He shall direct your paths.

Proverbs 3:5–6 NKJV

Your word is a lamp to my feet and a light for my path.

Psalm 119:105 NIV

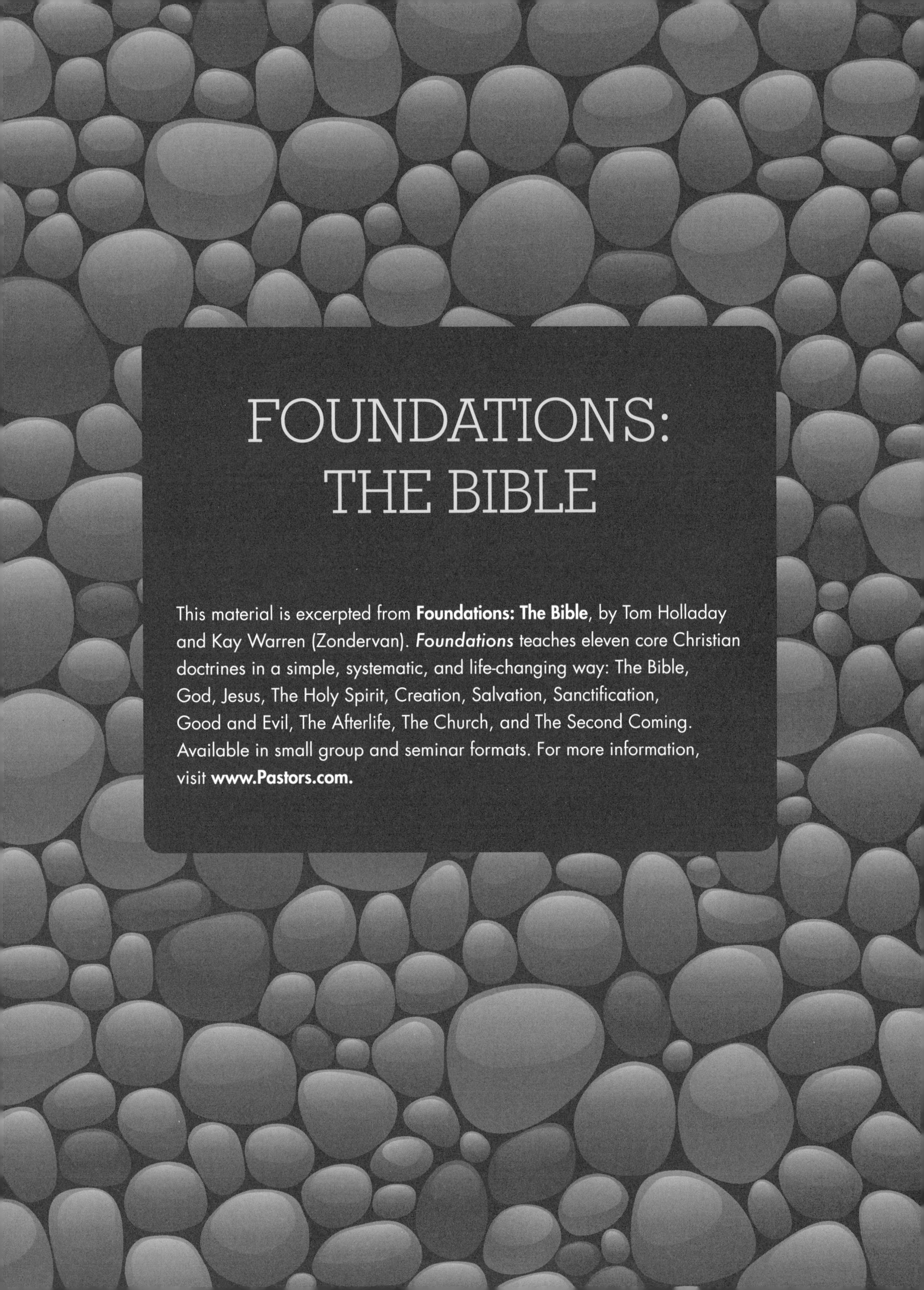
FOUNDATIONS:
THE BIBLE
This material is excerpted from **Foundations: The Bible**, by Tom Holladay and Kay Warren (Zondervan). *Foundations* teaches eleven core Christian doctrines in a simple, systematic, and life-changing way: The Bible, God, Jesus, The Holy Spirit, Creation, Salvation, Sanctification, Good and Evil, The Afterlife, The Church, and The Second Coming. Available in small group and seminar formats. For more information, visit **www.Pastors.com.**

How Do We Know the Bible Came from God?

You may be asking yourself, "If the Bible shows us who God really is, how do I know I can trust it? What makes it more trustworthy than any other book? Is there any objective evidence that the Bible is a unique book?"

YES! Every Christian needs to understand four classic proofs of the reliability of the Bible. These proofs answer the questions we hear from others and that you may be asking yourself: "Why should I trust the Bible more than any other book? What is so special about the Bible?"

FIRST: THE EXTERNAL EVIDENCE SAYS THE BIBLE IS A HISTORICAL BOOK.

External evidence simply means the proofs for the reliability of the Bible that are outside the pages of the Bible itself. For instance:

- ***The number of manuscript copies and the short length of time between the original manuscripts and our first copies of the New Testament***

Norman Geisler writes:

> For the New Testament the evidence is overwhelming. There are 5,366 manuscripts to compare and draw information from, and some of these date from the second or third centuries. To put that in perspective, there are only 643 copies of Homer's ***Iliad***, and that is the most famous book of ancient Greece! No one doubts the existence of Julius Caesar's ***Gallic Wars***, but we only have 10 copies of it and the earliest of those was made 1,000 years after it was written. To have such an abundance of copies of the New Testament from dates within 70 years after their writing is amazing.[2]
>
> —Norman Geisler

[2] Norman L. Geisler and Ronald M. Brooks, *When Skeptics Ask* (Wheaton, IL: Victor, 1990), 159–160.

Why didn't God allow us to have the original rather than relying on a number of copies? One possibility: we would have worshiped an old document rather than reading and following his living Word.

By the way, it's important to understand that Bibles are translated from these original copies, which were written in Hebrew, Aramaic, and Greek. Many people have the idea that the Bible has been passed down from language to language over the centuries, and thus may have been changed many times. That's not true. When a Bible translation is done, the translator goes back to these early manuscripts in the original languages.

- *The extreme care with which the Scriptures were copied*

The earliest Jewish scribes (Old Testament copyists) followed a strict code to insure accuracy in their copies. Here are a few of the rules they followed meticulously:

1. Each scroll must contain a specified number of columns, all equal throughout the entire book.
2. The length of each column must not be less than forty-eight lines or more than sixty lines.
3. Each column's breadth must be exactly thirty letters.
4. The copyist must use a specially prepared black ink.
5. The copyist must not copy from memory.
6. The space between every consonant must be the size of a thread.
7. The copyist must sit in full Jewish dress.
8. The copyist must use a fresh quill to pen the sacred name of God. (The copyists held the Scriptures and the name of God in such reverence that they would even refuse to acknowledge the presence of a king while writing the name they held so holy.)

Later scribes added these requirements:

1. They could copy only letter by letter, not word by word.
2. They counted the number of times each letter of the alphabet occurred in each book, and if it came out wrong, they threw the scroll away.
3. They knew the middle letter of the Pentateuch (the first five books of the Old Testament) and the middle letter of the entire Old Testament. After copying a scroll, they counted forward and backward from this middle letter. If the number of letters did not match what they knew to be correct, they destroyed the scroll and started over.

• *Confirmation of places and dates by archaeology*

The confirmation through archaeological findings of places and dates helps many to see the reliability of the Bible.

The Dead Sea Scrolls are one of the most famous archaeological discoveries. What's so significant about them? Every one of the Old Testament books is found in these scrolls. Before their discovery, the earliest manuscripts we had of some of the Old Testament books were from 900 A.D.—almost a thousand years later than when these scrolls were made. Amazingly, when the Dead Sea Scrolls were compared with the later manuscripts, practically no differences were found. (The differences, about 5 percent, are mostly in word spellings.) That's almost no changes in 1,000 years!

The Bible's historical accuracy has been questioned repeatedly through the years, yet again and again, archaeology has proven the Bible to be right and the critics wrong. Erwin Lutzer writes in *Seven Reasons Why You Can Trust the Bible*:

Here are some examples of where critics have had to change their mind about the Bible's reliability.

- For years critics insisted that the story of Abram's rescue of Lot in Genesis 14 was not historically accurate. They said (1) that the names of the kings listed were fictitious, since they were not confirmed in secular histories; (2) that the idea that the king of Babylon was serving the king of Elam was historically impossible. . . . But archaeology had debunked these critics. The names of some of the kings have now been identified. And there is evidence that the king of Babylon did serve the king of Elam at this time.

- For decades it was said that the Old Testament writers invented the Hittite tribe, since their existence could not be independently confirmed. However, in 1911–12 Professor Hugo Winchkler of Berlin discovered some ten thousand clay tablets at Bogazkoy, the site of the Hittite capital. The existence of the Hittite empire is now extensively proven and documented.

- The existence of Solomon's reign and his thousands of horses was at one time questioned. But in Meggido, which was one of five chariot cities, excavations have revealed the ruins of thousands of stalls for his horses and chariots.[3]

Archaeology confirms that the places and people the Bible speaks about were historically accurate. This is true not only of the Old Testament but also of the relatively more recent history of the New Testament. Archaeologists have uncovered many of the places where New Testament events occurred. A few examples: portions of Herod's temple, the Areopagus in which Paul spoke in Athens, the theater in Ephesus where Acts 19 tells us a riot occurred, the pool of Siloam where a man was healed of blindness in John 9. *The Book of Acts* is a model of historical accuracy. "In all, Luke names thirty-two countries, fifty-four cities, and nine islands without error."[4]

William Albright reminds us:

Discovery after discovery has established the accuracy of innumerable details, and has brought increased recognition to the value of the Bible as a source of history.[5]

—William F. Albright

[3] Erwin Lutzer, *Seven Reasons Why You Can Trust the Bible* (Chicago: Moody Press, 1998), 73.

[4] Norman Geisler, *Baker Encyclopedia of Apologetics* (Grand Rapids, MI: Baker, 1999), 47.

[5] William F. Albright, *The Archeology of Palestine* (Harmondsworth, Middlesex: Pelican, 1960), 127.

SECOND: THE INTERNAL EVIDENCE SAYS THE BIBLE IS A UNIQUE BOOK

Internal evidence is the evidence that you see in the Bible itself. If you never studied archaeology or history, you could still see the reliability of the Bible just by reading it. Look with me at just two of the ways we can see from the pages of the Bible that it is trustworthy and unique.

- ***The majority of the Bible is from eyewitness accounts***

  We all know the value of an eyewitness. When a prosecutor can call upon someone who saw what happened, the prosecution has a much greater chance of winning a conviction.

  One piece of evidence that historians look for in assessing the reliability of any document is the number of generations that passed on a story before that story was written down. In other words, is the information firsthand or secondhand? The events of the Bible were primarily recorded in the generation in which they were experienced—by those who experienced them!

  The Bible is filled with eyewitness accounts. Moses was there when the Red Sea split. Joshua saw with his own eyes the wall of Jericho falling. The disciples stood together in the Upper Room and saw and heard the resurrected Lord Jesus.

- ***The amazing agreement and consistency throughout the Bible***

  Josh McDowell writes,

  > The Bible was written over a period of about 1,500 years in various places stretching all the way from Babylon to Rome. The human authors included over 40 persons from various stations of life: kings, peasants, poets, herdsmen, fishermen, scientists, farmers, priests, pastors, tent-makers and governors. It was written in a wilderness, a dungeon, inside palaces and prisons, on lonely islands and in military battles. Yet it speaks with agreement and reliability on hundreds of controversial subjects. Yet it tells one story from beginning to end, God's salvation of man through Jesus Christ. NO PERSON could have possibly conceived of or written such a work![6]
  >
  > —Josh McDowell

[6] Josh McDowell, *Evidence that Demands a Verdict* (San Bernardino, Calif.: Communications, 1988), 5.

A CLOSER LOOK

What's the Difference?

The Bible is translated from 24,000 copies of the New Testament alone, with millions of people having seen some of these copies. Those copies have been translated by thousands of scholars.	**The Book of Mormon** is translated from a supposed single original that is claimed to have been seen and translated by one man: Joseph Smith (who was not an expert in languages). That original was "taken back." There are no copies of that original.
The Bible was written by more than forty different authors spanning over fifty generations and three continents. It speaks with agreement on all matters of faith and doctrine.	**The Qu'ran** is the writings and record of one man, Muhammad, in one place at one point in history. It differs at many points with the Old and New Testament accounts of history.
The Bible provides God's distinctive solution to man's problem with sin and focuses on God's work in actual, verifiable history.	**Hindu** scriptures claim all roads lead to the same place and focus on stories of things that happened in the "celestial realms."

THIRD: THE PERSONAL EVIDENCE SAYS THE BIBLE IS A POWERFUL BOOK

The Bible is the world's best-selling book. Most people know that it was the first major book to be printed on a press (the Gutenberg Bible). The Bible, in whole or in part, has been translated into more than 1,300 languages.

Millions of lives have been changed through the truth in the Bible!

The truth of the Bible has changed my life. I can't tell you how many times just the right word at just the right time gave me God's direction at a crossroad.

Tom Holladay writes:

I remember the struggle I faced when my mother was in the last stages of cancer. She lived about a two-hour drive from the town I was living in. Once a week or so, I would drive through the valley and over the curvy mountain roads to spend a few hours with her. Although her tenacious spirit never allowed her to admit it, we all knew she didn't have long to live. She was a believer in Jesus Christ, and I was filled with a strong faith that she was heading for an eternity of joy in heaven. However, I was unprepared for the waves of emotion that would hit me as I watched her slipping away, the wave of her body growing weaker, the wave of her mind becoming confused. I felt drenched by the realities of her illness. Oh, I wanted her to be with the Lord, but not this soon and not like this. Everything in me wanted to do something to stop this. So I got on the activity merry-go-round. Frantically, I chased after ways to stop what was happening to my mother. Even if it had nothing to do with my mom, I found myself constantly doing things to try to ease my hurting. (Please know that I'm not saying we shouldn't do all we possibly can for someone we love. My activities, however, were often nothing more than pointless exertion of energy.)

One night as I was driving home after seeing her, weariness overwhelmed me. As I rounded one dark curve after another, I was struck again and again with the thought: How could I possibly help my mother when I didn't even have the strength to face the fact that she was dying?

At that moment, Jesus' words from Matthew 11:28 pierced my soul: ***"Come to me, all you who are weary and burdened, and I will give you rest."***

"I will give you rest!" The experience of these words coming into my mind was so powerful and personal; I could almost sense that Jesus was riding with me in that car. In the perfect timing of God, at that moment I rounded the last curve through the mountains and saw the expanse and the lights of the valley spread out in front of me. The thought hit me: God wants to broaden my perspective, to help me be aware of the fact that he is working even when I can't. "I will give you rest." I must have repeated those words to myself hundreds of times during the weeks leading up to my mother's death. The hurt was real, but God's promise made his presence and strength just as real. His promise gave me the perspective I needed to face the death of my mother.

—Tom Holladay

Remember, personal testimony is just one of the four proofs that the Bible is God's book.

People talk about how the *Book of Mormon* has changed their life, or how the *Qu'ran* has made a difference, or even describe the impact of a line from the latest Star Wars movie!

This, too, is personal testimony. It's subjective, meaning it is the account of one person's experience that has no objective proof.

The good news is, the Bible is shown to be reliable by both objective proof and subjective experience. You can see in the facts of archaeology and history that the Bible is a trustworthy book. And you can see in the personal experience of billions that the Bible is a book that changes lives.

FOURTH: JESUS SAID THE BIBLE CAME FROM GOD

Have you ever heard someone say, "I trust what Jesus said, but not the rest of the Bible"? Jesus himself spoke with confidence about the Bible. If we trust what Jesus said, we have no choice but to trust all of the Bible.

1. **Jesus recognized the Spirit as the AUTHOR.**

> ***"Why, then," Jesus asked, "did the Spirit inspire David to call him 'Lord'? David said, 'The Lord said to my Lord: Sit here at my right side until I put your enemies under your feet.'"***
>
> **Matthew 22:43–44 (GNT)**

Jesus, quoting from what David wrote in the Psalms, recognizes that the Spirit inspired David's words.

2. **Jesus quoted the Bible as AUTHORITATIVE.**

In Matthew 22:29 Jesus told the Sadducees that not knowing the Scriptures was the reason they lived in error and without God's power.

> ***Jesus replied, "You are in error because you do not know the Scriptures or the power of God."***
>
> **Matthew 22:29 (NIV)**

In Luke 11 Jesus clearly tells us that God's Word is not just history or poetry; it is to be obeyed.

> ***He replied, "Blessed rather are those who hear the word of God and obey it."***
>
> **Luke 11:28 (NIV)**

3. **Jesus proclaimed its uniqueness.**

Jesus reminded us that the Bible stands above all other books and all other writings. In fact, he told us that this book stands above all that we see in this physical universe.

Read with me what Jesus said in Matthew 5:18 and in John 10:35:

> ***I tell you the truth, until heaven and earth disappear, not the smallest letter, not the least stroke of a pen, will by any means disappear from the Law until everything is accomplished.***
>
> **Matthew 5:18 (NIV)**

> ***Scripture is always true.***
>
> **John 10:35 (NCV)**

4. **Jesus called it the "WORD OF GOD."**

> ***Thus you nullify the word of God by your tradition that you have handed down. And you do many things like that.***
>
> **Mark 7:13 (NIV)**

Even though Jesus did not possess the original writings of the Bible by Moses, David, and so forth, he nevertheless considered the manuscript copies used in his day to be "the word of God." This is a powerful and personal expression to us of the truth that God works to preserve the integrity and accuracy of the Bible through generation after generation.

5. Jesus believed that people and places in the Bible were real.

- **He believed in the PROPHETS (Matthew 22:40; 24:15).**
- **He believed in NOAH (Luke 17:26).**
- **He believed in ADAM and EVE (Matthew 19:4).**
- **He believed in SODOM and GOMORRAH (Matthew 10:15).**
- **He believed in JONAH (Matthew 12:40).**

It's interesting that these last four (Noah, Adam and Eve, Sodom and Gomorrah, and Jonah) are found in the portions of the Bible most often attacked as fables or just good stories by those who distrust its historical reliability. The very parts of the Bible that are doubted today are affirmed by the words of Jesus himself.

John MacArthur writes:

> The Bible is the only completely trustworthy source of knowledge about God. Man can't learn all he needs to know about God from human reason, philosophy, or even experience. God alone is the source of the knowledge about Himself, and He has chosen to reveal Himself in the Bible and in no other book.[7]
>
> —John MacArthur Jr.

I want to make sure that as we discuss the historical reliability of the Bible, we keep in mind its impact on our lives.

Though the Bible is the record of how God revealed himself to men and women down through history, he gave us this book to personally reveal to us what he is like. He gave us this book to change our lives.

Before we go on, I'd like you to answer in your minds two intensely personal and incredibly important questions about this book:

First, what changes has God's Word worked in your life, or what changes would you like to see the truth of God's Word bring about in your life?

Take a moment to think about that.

[7] John MacArthur Jr., *Is the Bible Reliable?* (Panorama City, CA: Word of Grace Communications, 1988), 5.

Second, how has this book, the Bible, shown you who God really is, or how do you need God to reveal himself to you through this book?

Again, take a moment.

~~~~~~~~~~~~~~~~~~

As we continue in this study, I believe you'll have a greater confidence that the Bible you hold in your hand is God's Word—not just in part but in whole. You'll also be better able to explain to someone else—a friend or your children—the foundation upon which that belief is built.

We've looked at four tests, or proofs, of the Bible's reliability. By every one of these four tests—external, internal, personal, and scriptural—the words of the Bible are clearly shown to be God's revelation to the people of every generation. There is, however, one nagging question that continues to bother some people regarding the reliability of the Bible.
~~~~~~~~~~~~~~~~~~

How Do We Know We Have the Right Books?

A common misconception is that although God may have written the Bible, the books that are included in it were chosen by a committee of men who could have easily left out some books. Let's clear that up and look at the truth. The bottom line is that if God wrote the books, he is certainly powerful enough to make sure those books are included in his Word. Here are three reasons we know that we have the right books.

THE TESTIMONY OF THE BIBLE

- *Jesus recognized the Old Testament canon. The word "canon" refers to the list of books that are accepted as Scripture.*

Jesus said:

> ***This is what I told you while I was still with you: Everything must be fulfilled that is written about me in the Law of Moses, the Prophets and the Psalms.***
>
> **Luke 24:44 (NIV)**

When Jesus mentions the Law, the Prophets, and the Psalms in Luke 24, he is affirming all three major divisions of the Old Testament.

- *Peter recognized part of the New Testament canon.*

Peter wrote:

> ***Some things in Paul's letters are hard to understand, and people who are ignorant and weak in faith explain these things falsely. They also falsely explain the other Scriptures, but they are destroying themselves by doing this.***
>
> **2 Peter 3:16 (NCV)**

Circle the words "the other Scriptures" (on the previous page). These letters of Paul had just been written, and they were already being recognized as Scripture by the church.

- *Paul recognized the EQUAL inspiration of the Old and New Testaments in a single verse.*

For the Scripture says,

> ***"Do not muzzle an ox while it is treading out the grain," and "The worker deserves his wages."***
>
> **1 Timothy 5:18 (NIV)**

This is an amazing verse. In it Paul quotes from Deuteronomy 25:4 in the Old Testament and from Luke 10:7 in the New Testament, and calls them both Scripture!

Students of Bible history believe that Luke's Gospel was written in 60 A.D. and that *The Book of First Timothy* was written in 63 A.D. This means that *The Gospel of Luke* was being recognized as Holy Scripture within only three years of its writing.

THE HISTORY OF THE CHURCH

When you look at how books actually came to be included in the Bible, you realize that it was not the result of one vote taken at a single meeting.

Books were included in the New Testament on the basis of three things:

1. **The authority of an APOSTLE**

   The New Testament stands on the foundation of the apostles, men who intimately knew Jesus. God decided to use those who were closest to Jesus to tell the story of his life and to show us how to live as Jesus lived.

   The New Testament has eyewitness authority. Take the writers of the Gospels, for instance. Matthew was an apostle, Mark wrote down Peter's remembrances, Luke was a friend of Paul, and John was an apostle.

2. **The teaching of the TRUTH**

The first people to read the New Testament books saw the light of God's truth in them. The clear ring of truth in the words caused them to see these books as something entirely different from other religious writings of that day.

As more and more people read these books, a third affirmation resulted:

3. **The confirmation of the CHURCH**

Many people think that the New Testament books were chosen by a council of a few people. That is not true. A council did recognize the books of the New Testament (around 400 A.D.), but that was after the church had been using these books for 300 years. The council formally recognized the books in response to false teachers who were trying to add books to the Bible.

The misconception is that what gives these books authority is the fact that they were "voted in." The opposite is true. What caused these books to be recognized as God's Word is the fact that these books had the authority of God behind them.

THE POWER OF GOD

> ***The grass withers and the flowers fall, but the word of our God stands forever.***
>
> **Isaiah 40:8 (NIV)**

Our assurance that we have the right books is a matter of FAITH. God would not have allowed any part of what he had chosen to stand forever to be left out.

You can erase from your mind the thought that someday they'll discover in some cave a book of the Bible that should have gotten in—a "lost" book of the Bible. Do you think God would let that happen? Of course not!

BIBLE STUDY METHODS

Twelve Ways You Can Unlock God's Word

"The Spirit of God uses the Word of God to make us like the Son of God."

–Rick Warren in ***The Purpose Driven® Life***

You were created to become like Christ. This is one of the five God-ordained purposes for your life described in ***The Purpose Driven® Life*** by Rick Warren, and it's why studying the Bible is so important. The Bible's truths will transform you, aligning you with the character and ways of Jesus as you encounter him in the Scriptures. ***Rick Warren's Bible Study Methods*** is an easy-to-understand book that shows you how to study the Bible Rick Warren's way. It gives you not just one, but twelve methods for exploring the riches of God's Word. At least one of them is exactly what you're looking for—an approach that's right for you, right where you're at. Simple step-by-step instructions guide you through the how-to's of the following methods: Devotional, Chapter Summary, Character Quality, Thematic, Biographical, Topical, Word Study, Book Background, Book Survey, Chapter Analysis, Book Synthesis, and Verse Analysis.

Preview of the 12 Bible Study Methods

In his book *Rick Warren's Bible Study Methods*, Pastor Rick Warren presents and explains twelve proven Bible study methods that will enable you to study the Bible on your own. They are given in the order of simplicity and use of reference tools, beginning with the easiest and moving on to the harder ones.

1. ***The Devotional Method.*** Select a short portion of your Bible and prayerfully meditate on it until the Holy Spirit shows you a way to apply the truth to your life. Write out a personal application.

2. ***The Chapter Summary Method.*** Read a chapter of a Bible book through at least five times; then write down a summary of the central thoughts you find in it.

3. ***The Character Quality Method.*** Choose a character quality you would like to work on in your life and study what the Bible says about it.

4. ***The Thematic Method.*** Select a Bible theme to study. Then think of three to five questions you'd like to have answered about that theme. Next, study all the references you can find on your theme and record the answers to your questions.

5. ***The Biographical Method.*** Select a Bible character and research all the verses about that person in order to study his life and characteristics. Make notes on his attitudes, strengths, and weaknesses. Then apply what you have learned to your own life.

6. ***The Topical Method.*** Collect and compare all the verses you can find on a particular topic. Organize your conclusions into an outline that you can share with another person.

7. ***The Word Study Method.*** Study the important words of the Bible. Find out how many times a word occurs in Scripture and how it is used. Find out the original meaning of the word.

8. ***The Book Background Method.*** Study how history, geography, culture, science, and politics affected what happened in Bible times. Use Bible reference books to increase your understanding of the Word.

9. ***The Book Survey Method.*** Survey an entire book of the Bible by reading it through several times to get a general overview of its subject matter. Study the background of the book and make notes on its contents.

10. ***The Chapter Analysis Method.*** Master the contents of a chapter of a book of the Bible by taking an in-depth look at each verse in that chapter. Take each verse apart word by word, observing every detail.

11. ***The Book Synthesis Method.*** Summarize the contents and main themes of a book of the Bible after you have read it through several times. Make an outline of the book. This method can be done after you have used the Book Survey Method and the Chapter Analysis Method on every chapter of that book.

12. ***The Verse-by-Verse Analysis Method.*** Select one passage of Scripture and examine it in detail by asking questions, finding cross-references, and paraphrasing each verse. Record a possible application of each verse you study.

The Chapter Summary Method of Bible Study

HOW TO BEGIN UNDERSTANDING CHAPTERS OF A BOOK OF THE BIBLE

The Bible as it was originally written had no chapter or verse divisions. In fact, it wasn't until A.D. 1228 that Bishop Stephen Langton added the chapter divisions. These were added to make the various sections of the Bible more accessible to the readers. Some of these divisions are arbitrary and interrupt the flow of a writer's message. Usually, however, they provide good breaking points that are helpful in Bible study.

According to these divisions, there are 1,189 chapters in the Bible. If you studied one chapter each day, you could read through the Scriptures in just over three years. If you summarized two chapters a day, you could finish in about 20 months. This pace is certainly not recommended, because you could quickly get bored with the study method. Instead, select random chapters of Scripture that you want to study and use the summary method on those passages; or use a different method for variety.

Definition

The Chapter Summary Method of Bible Study involves gaining a general understanding of the contents of a chapter of the Bible by reading it through at least five times, asking a series of content questions, and summarizing the central thoughts of the passage. (This method should not be confused with the Book Survey and Chapter Analysis Methods—chapters 9 and 10 in *Rick Warren's Bible Study Methods*.)

Why This Method Is Important

This method is important because it enables you to begin understanding chapters of the books of the Bible. It is a popular method for those beginning Bible study because chapters are usually fairly short, and it does not require deep study to do a chapter summary. It is a valuable method because it can be quickly learned by a brand-new Christian or someone else who is interested in doing meaningful Bible study. It is an excellent method with which to begin a lifetime of personal Bible study, for four reasons:

1. **This method is easy to learn.** You can begin practicing it as soon as you understand the 10 basic steps that follow in the next section. The study form and example at the end of the chapter should help you.

2. **This method does not take much time.** Depending on the length of the chapter you are studying, you can complete a chapter summary in about 20 to 30 minutes. This is especially true if the chapter contains a historical narrative—parts of the Old Testament, the Gospels, and the book of Acts, for example. You will have to spend more time, however, in the Psalms, the prophetic books, and the doctrinal letters of the New Testament.

3. **This method does not require any outside help or reference tools, but it is necessary to memorize the ten steps.** Then you can do a chapter summary in any situation at any time, using your Bible and a piece of paper. Whenever you have extra time to spend—as in a doctor's waiting room, a bus depot, or an airport—this is the method to use. Pick a book of the Bible, start with chapter 1, and begin recording your discoveries. I like to use this method when I go to a retreat and cannot take my reference tools with me.

4. **This method is a good type of study to use when you are engaged in a rapid reading survey through the Bible.** You can make initial notes as you read each chapter by using the Chapter Summary Form.

Step One — Caption

Step Two — Contents

Step Three — Chief People

Step Four — Choice Verse

Step Five — Crucial Word(s)

Step Six — Challenges

Step Seven — Cross-References

Step Eight — Christ Seen

Step Nine — Central Lesson(s)

Step Ten — Conclusion

Ten Easy Steps for Doing a Chapter Summary

In preparing to fill in the study form for this method of Bible study, *read through the chapter at least five times.* You will find no better way to get acquainted with a chapter of the Bible than to read it over and over again. The more times you read a passage of Scripture, the more it will come alive to you. Many Christians miss the great insights of Scripture because they fail to read and reread its passages.

The great Bible expositor G. Campbell Morgan was famous for his powerful, exciting sermons. When asked for the secret of his ability to communicate God's Word, he replied that he made it a habit to read a chapter or passage 30 or 40 times before he began working on it for a sermon. It is no wonder his sermons were exciting and meaningful.

Here are some tips on how to read a chapter of the Bible:

- **Read it in a Bible without notes.** If you try using this method by reading a Bible in which you have made notes, you will have the tendency to concentrate on the same ideas. Let God speak to you in a fresh way and give you new insights.
- **Read it without stopping.** During your first few readings, don't stop in the middle of a chapter, but read it from start to finish. Your goal is to feel the flow of the chapter, so don't be concerned with the details at the outset. Try to capture the central message and the writer's overall theme.
- **Read it in several different contemporary translations.** This will give you additional insights as you see how each translator rendered the original writing. Make notes on the interesting differences you find.
- **Read it aloud quietly to yourself.** If you have a problem with concentration, this will help tremendously because you will be hearing yourself read. Many people have found that reading aloud helps them better focus their attention on the text.

As you are rereading the chapter, begin looking for the following 10 specific things and write your answers on your Chapter Summary Form or on a blank piece of paper. You may fill in the 10 Cs in any order, saving Step Ten for the last step. The 10 parts of your study are:

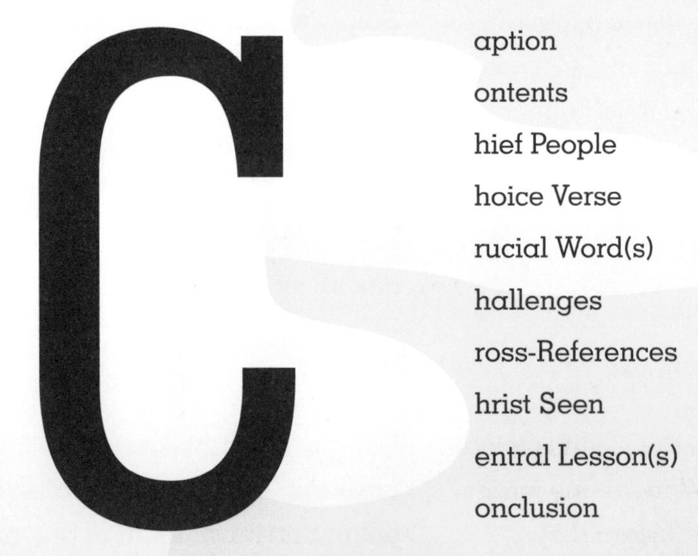

Step One—Caption

Give the chapter a short, descriptive title. The shorter the title, the more likely you will remember it. In fact, if you use this method on every chapter in a selected book of the Bible, you can remember the contents of the whole book by memorizing your chapter titles. Use one word if possible (1 Corinthians 13 might be titled "Love") and five words at most (Hebrews 11 could be "Heroes of the Faith"). Try to find the key word of the chapter and fit it into your title. If your title is catchy or produces a mental picture, you will remember it longer. One creative person gave "Well-Well" as a title for John 4. The two key events of that chapter are the woman at the ***well*** and the nobleman's son whom Jesus made ***well***.

Step Two—Contents

Describe, summarize, paraphrase, outline, or make a list of the major points in a chapter. The method you choose will depend on the literary style of the chapter and on your own preference. Some people like to summarize; analytical people enjoy outlining. Choose the method with which you feel most comfortable and that is easy for you to do. Don't try to interpret the chapter; just make observations on its contents. Record on your form what you feel the writer said.

Step Three—Chief People

List the most important people in the chapter. Ask questions such as: ***Who are the main people in this chapter? Why are they included? What is significant about them?*** If the chapter contains pronouns (***he, she, they, etc.***) you may have to refer to the previous chapter to identify the people. Write down your reasons for choosing certain people as the chief ones of the chapter. When you come to long genealogies (lists of people), don't try to list each one, but summarize the list.

Step Four—Choice Verse

Choose a verse that summarizes the whole chapter or one that speaks to you personally. In some chapters you may find a key verse that summarizes the writer's argument; in other chapters there may not be a key verse. On occasion you may want to pick a verse from which you will be writing your application, a verse that you believe God would have you apply to your life.

Step Five—Crucial Word(s)

Write down the key word or words of the chapter. Many times the key word will be the one that is used most frequently ("love" in 1 Corinthians 13 and "faith" in Hebrews 11). Sometimes the crucial word may be the most important word but not the most used one. In Romans 6, for example, the word "count" (KJV, "reckon") is the important word even though it is used only once (Romans 6:11). Also, a chapter may have more than one crucial word.

Step Six—Challenges

List any difficulties you may have with the passage. Are there any statements you do not understand? Is there any problem or question you would like to study further?

Often while doing a chapter summary you will get ideas for other types of studies you may want to do in the future. For instance, a certain word in the chapter may catch your attention. Take note of that word; later you may want to do an in-depth study of it (see chapter 7 of *Rick Warren's Bible Study Methods*). A question about a doctrinal matter might motivate you to do a topical study on that particular teaching (see chapter 6 of *Rick Warren's Bible Study Methods*).

Step Seven—Cross-References

Using the cross-references in your study Bible, look up other verses that help clarify what the chapter is talking about and list them on your form. Ask the question, ***"What else in the Bible helps me understand this chapter?"*** Cross-references are important because they are helpful tools in interpreting the meaning of a chapter; they enable you to see what the Bible as a whole has to say on any given teaching. You can look for several types of cross-references, described in the section on correlation in the Chapter Analysis Method (see chapter 10 of *Rick Warren's Bible Study Methods*) and in chapter 10 of Walter Henrichsen and Gayle Jackson's book *Studying, Interpreting, and Applying the Bible* (Zondervan).

Step Eight—Christ Seen

The entire Bible is a revelation of the person of Jesus Christ. In fact, Jesus used the Old Testament to teach his disciples about himself. On the day of resurrection on the Emmaus road, Jesus taught two of his disciples: "*Beginning with Moses and all the Prophets, he explained to them what was said in all the Scriptures concerning himself*" (Luke 24:27). As you study each chapter, be alert for statements that tell you something about Jesus Christ, the Holy Spirit, or God the Father. Ask yourself, ***"What can I learn about the nature of Jesus from this chapter?" "What attributes of God in Christ are illustrated here?"*** (Some examples: his love, justice, mercy, holiness, power, and faithfulness.) This step may be the most difficult to complete in some portions of the Bible, particularly in Old Testament narratives and in passages where symbolism is used.

Step Nine—Central Lesson(s)

Write down the major principles, insights, and lessons you learn from this chapter. Ask yourself, ***Why does God want this passage in the Bible? What does he want to teach me from this chapter? What is the central thought the writer is trying to develop?*** A possible answer might be, "*We should be loving in all interpersonal relationships*" (1 Corinthians 13).

Step Ten—Conclusion

This is the application portion of your study. As discussed in chapter 1, develop a project to help you implement in your life a lesson you have learned from the chapter. It will benefit you to conclude your chapter summary by asking yourself two questions: ***"How do these truths apply to me personally?"*** And, ***"What specifically am I going to do about them?"***

HOW TO FILL IN THE CHAPTER SUMMARY FORM

At the end of this chapter you will find a "Chapter Summary Form" that you can reproduce for your own use. The form has a place for listing the chapter of the Bible you are studying and the 10 steps of this method. Fill in the blank spaces for each of the 10 parts just described. If you need more room, use the back of the form or allow more room on your own paper.

Sample Filled-Out Form

See the examples at the end of this chapter.

Assignment

Some chapters on which you can start using the "Chapter Summary Method of Bible Study" are:

- 1 Corinthians 13
- 2 Timothy 2
- 1 John 1
- John 17
- The Gospel of Luke (chapter-by-chapter)

For Further Reading

The Summarized Bible by Keith L. Brooks (Baker). This book is an excellent example of this method of Bible study. Dr. Brooks offers a chapter summary on every chapter of every book in the Bible and shows how Jesus Christ may be seen in each chapter. Don't read this book to help you do the study; only use it afterward to check to see how you have done on your own.

Chapter Summary Form

CHAPTER *Luke 15* Read 5 times √ (check when done)

1. CAPTION (Title)

   "Lost and Found"

2. CONTENTS (This chapter contains three parables.)

   1. Verses 3–7: The lost sheep

   2. Verses 8–10: The lost coin

   3. Verses 11–32: The lost son

3. CHIEF PEOPLE

   The shepherd with the lost sheep

   The woman with the lost coin

   The father with the lost son

4. CHOICE VERSE

   Luke 15:7 — "I tell you that in the same way there will be more rejoicing in heaven over one sinner who repents than over ninety-nine righteous persons who do not need to repent."

5. CRUCIAL WORD(S)

   Lost (vv. 4, 5, 9, 24, 32)

   Found (vv. 5–6, 9, 24, 32)

6. CHALLENGES (Difficulties I need to study.)

   What does this verse mean — "ninety-nine righteous persons who do not need to repent?"

7. CROSS-REFERENCES, Luke 15:4–6

Matthew 18:11–14

John 10:10–14

Isaiah 53:6

1 Peter 2:25

Psalm 119:176

8. CHRIST SEEN

1st Parable—Jesus the Good Shepherd searching for lost sheep.

2nd Parable— The Holy Spirit our rightful Owner finding and restoring.

3rd Parable—God the Father waiting to welcome us home.

9. CENTRAL LESSON(S)

INSIGHTS

The son went away saying, "Give me" (v. 12).

He returned saying, "Make me" (v. 19).

God cares for sinners and anxiously waits for them to return home.

CHARACTERISTICS OF THE IMMATURE BROTHER

Anger—v. 28

Childish—v. 28

Jealousy—vv. 29–30

Wrong perspective—vv. 29–30

Grumbling—vv. 29–30

10. CONCLUSION (Personal Application)

In each of the three parables a concrete effort was made to recover what was lost. Many of my friends are lost without Christ. I need to develop specific witnessing plans for reaching them with the Good News. I will start by sharing my faith with my friend Jim this weekend.

I need to express more joy when I hear of people who have accepted Christ.

Chapter Summary Form

CHAPTER Read 5 times ☐ (check when done)

1. CAPTION (Title)

2. CONTENTS

3. CHIEF PEOPLE

4. CHOICE VERSE

5. CRUCIAL WORD(S)

6. CHALLENGES (Difficulties I need to study.)

7. CROSS-REFERENCES

8. CHRIST SEEN

9. CENTRAL LESSON(S)

10. CONCLUSION (Personal Application)

The Character Quality Method of Bible Study

HOW TO DETERMINE BIBLICAL CHARACTER QUALITIES

A major goal of Christian living is to develop Christlike character in our lives. Daily we want to become more and more like Jesus Christ by replacing bad character qualities with good ones. But before we can work on a Christlike quality in our lives, we must be able to recognize it. This study is designed to help you identify negative and positive character qualities and then be able to understand them.

You may then work on setting aside negative character qualities and building positive ones in your life. Doing these things will enable you to become more and more like Jesus Christ.

Definition

The Character Quality Method of Bible Study involves finding what the Bible says about a particular characteristic of a person, with a heavy emphasis on personal application. Furthermore, it is a combination in simplified form of three other Bible study methods: the Word Study Method, the Biographical Method, and the Cross-Reference Method.

It differs from the Biographical Method in that here you are studying the characteristics of a person rather than the person himself. These qualities can be negative or positive or both. The point is that we learn to avoid the negative ones and work on building the positive ones into our lives.

Why This Method Is Vital for Our Lives

The purpose of this method of Bible study is to *identify* character qualities taught in the Bible with the view of learning to avoid the negative ones and learning to work on the positive ones, so that we become more like the Lord Jesus Christ. It is obvious that until we know what a character quality is, we cannot avoid it or develop it. For example, if we wanted to become meek, as the Bible admonishes us to be, we would have to know what meekness is before we could really study it.

This is the first method in this book that requires the use of some tools. So let us look at some of the reference tools you will need. (See **Tools for Effective Bible Study** on page 170 of this workbook for an explanation of these and other tools.)

1. A study Bible
2. An exhaustive concordance
3. A Bible dictionary and/or a word study book
4. A topical Bible
5. An English dictionary

If you want to develop positive biblical character qualities in your life, follow these tips:

1. **Only work on one quality at a time.** Don't try to work on two or three or more, for it takes concentrated effort to see how that one quality applies to every area of your life. It is far better to build one quality solidly into your life than to work on several weak ones.

2. **Don't rush it!** Character development takes time. Even though one of the steps is writing out an illustration after one week, you should probably want to work on one quality for a much longer time. I've found in my own life that God works on an area for months (sometimes years) before it becomes part of my daily walk with him.

3. **Stay with that one quality until you get victory in that specific area.** Don't skip around, trying to work on many qualities, when you need victory in that one. Remember that the quality of diligence is one you want to work on.

4. **Be alert to a negative quality in your life that is actually a positive one being misused.** Realize that the Lord wants to turn your weak points into strong ones. If you are rigid, legalistic, and unbending, it might be that the quality of self-discipline is being misused. That discipline needs to be tempered with compassion and concern for others.

5. **Trust the Holy Spirit to build these qualities in your life.** In the final analysis, it is God's power in you that reproduces the fruit of the Spirit in your life. It is God alone who can change your character. *"For it is God who works in you to will and to act according to his good purpose"* (Philippians 2:13). So let God do it, trusting the Holy Spirit to work in your life.

Step One—Name the Quality
Step Two—Name the Opposite Quality
Step Three—Do a Simple Word Study
Step Four—Find Some Cross-References
Step Five—Do a Brief Biographical Study
Step Six—Find a Memory Verse
Step Seven—Select a Situation or Relationship to Work On
Step Eight—Plan a Specific Project
Step Nine—Write Out a Personal Illustration

NINE STEPS FOR DOING A CHARACTER QUALITY STUDY

Step One—Name the Quality

Select the quality you want to study and write it down. Then look it up in an English dictionary and jot down the definition of that word or concept. List any synonyms or related words that help you understand this quality.

Step Two—Name the Opposite Quality

Write down the opposite quality—the antonym—of the one you are studying, and write out its dictionary definition and similar words. If you can't think of the opposite, use a dictionary of antonyms; some thesauruses also give antonyms. For example, ***unfaithfulness*** is the opposite of ***faithfulness***. But in some qualities you might be studying, there might be two or more opposites. For example, you could have the following:

- Faith and doubt
- Faith and apathy
- Faith and fear

Step Three—Do a Simple Word Study

Look up the Bible definition of the quality you are studying. Find the ways it is used in the scriptural contexts; then check a Bible dictionary, encyclopedia, or word study book for the way the quality was used in biblical times and in the Scriptures. Some of the tools will tell you how many times the word is used in the Bible, each testament, the writings of different authors, and in the book you are studying.

For example, if you were studying the quality of meekness, you would discover that the word ***meek*** in the original Greek meant "breaking something and bringing it under submission." The word was used to describe the training of valuable horses, which were brought under submission to their masters. A stallion would still have all the power and strength of its wild days, but it was now under its master's control. Meekness, therefore, is not weakness. As a Christian character quality, meekness is strength that is in submission to Jesus Christ.

Step Four—Find Some Cross-References

Using cross-references will give you additional insights from other portions of the Bible. Scripture is still the best interpreter of Scripture. Use your concordance and topical Bible to find all the verses you can relating to this quality. Look up the word and its synonyms in the concordance and topical Bible, write the cross-reference on the form in the appropriate section, and give a brief description of that verse. Then ask some of the following questions about the quality you are studying as you meditate on the cross-reference verses:

- What are the benefits this trait can bring me?
- What are some bad consequences this trait can bring me?
- What are the benefits this trait can bring to others?
- What are some bad consequences this trait can bring to others?
- Is there any promise from God related to this trait?
- Is there any warning or judgment related to this trait?
- Is there a command related to this trait?
- What factors produce this trait?
- Did Jesus have anything to say about this quality? What?
- What writer talked about this quality the most?
- Is this trait symbolized by anything in Scripture? Is that significant?
- Is this trait listed with a group of qualities? What is the relationship between them? What does this suggest?
- What Scriptures tell me directly what God thinks of this trait?
- Do I want more or less of this trait in my life?

After asking a series of questions such as these, or others that you think of, you might write a brief summary of the Bible's teaching on this quality. You may list any lessons or principles that you learned from this mini-topical study, or you may paraphrase a few key verses on this trait.

Always be sure to write down any difficulties you have with the verses you looked up, or questions you would like to see answered. Possibly, later on you will understand what is difficult at present and then find answers to your problems; often one verse sheds light on another verse you have studied.

Step Five—Do a Brief Biographical Study

Now go back to your Bible and try to find at least one person (more if possible) who showed this character quality in his or her life. Briefly describe this quality and write down the Scriptures that refer to it. Ask these questions as you do this part of the study:

- What shows this quality in his/her life?
- How did this quality affect his/her life?
- Did the quality help or hinder his/her growth to maturity? How?
- What results did it produce in his/her life?

An example of this step may be seen in the life of Joseph, the son of Jacob, who displayed different qualities of the fruit of the Spirit (Galatians 5:22–23) in each incident in his life. It is interesting to note his testimony before the heathen: *"So Pharaoh asked them, 'Can we find anyone like this man, one in whom is the Spirit of God?'"* (Genesis 41:38). We find these qualities in Joseph:

- He displayed ***love*** in a difficult family situation (Genesis 47).
- He displayed ***self-control*** in a difficult temptation (Genesis 39).
- He displayed industry and ***patience*** in difficult circumstances (Genesis 39:19–40:23).
- He displayed ***faithfulness*** in a difficult task (Genesis 41:37–57).
- He displayed ***goodness***, ***gentleness***, and ***kindness*** in difficult family reunions (Genesis 45:20).

Occasionally, some of the qualities the Bible teaches are evident in the ways of certain animals (particularly in *The Book of Proverbs*). When you find these qualities, write them down.

Step Six—Find a Memory Verse

Write down at least one verse from your cross-reference or biographical portion of the study that really speaks to you and that you intend to memorize during the following week. This verse should come in handy when God provides an opportunity for you to work on this character quality in a specific way.

Step Seven—Select a Situation or Relationship to Work On

We are now getting to the application part of the study. Think of an area in your life in which God wants you to work on this character quality—avoiding it if it's negative or building it up if it's positive. This can either be a situation or an interpersonal relationship.

If it is a situation, anticipate in advance what you will do when the situation arises. Suppose you have been slothful, lazy. Your study on slothfulness has challenged you to get rid of this quality in your life. As you plan ahead, you know when situations will arise that will bring out the lazy streak in you, so you decide ahead of time what you will do: You will set two alarm clocks, one on the far side of the room, to help you get up in the morning to have a quiet time and be on time to work or school.

If it is a relationship, then determine ahead of time how you will respond in your interactions with that person. This person could be your wife, husband, parents, children, girlfriend, boyfriend, work associates, school friends, or neighbors. Look for opportunities to work on that character quality in your relationships with that person or persons. Your goal is to have more mature relationships.

One way of doing this is to think back and recall a good situation or relationship in your recent past when you did work on this quality.

Step Eight—Plan a Specific Project

This is the practical part of your application and is the actual working out of Step Seven. Think of a project that you will work on to build a positive quality in your life or to get rid of a negative quality.

Once I was working on the trait of gratefulness. One of my projects was to write "grateful letters" to five people who had been a blessing to me, saying, "I am grateful for you because . . ." Remember: applications should be personal, practical, possible, and provable.

Step Nine—Write Out a Personal Illustration

A few days after you have completed the first eight steps of this study, write out an illustration of how you were able to work on this quality. This is the "provable" (measurable) part of your application. Be specific, and write down where you have succeeded and where you might have failed. In just a short time you should be able to develop a whole set of personal examples of how God is working in your life, getting rid of negative qualities and building positive ones.

These illustrations will serve a number of purposes. When you get discouraged, read over the backlog of your illustrations and see how God has worked in you. When you are working with someone who is a "Timothy," use your illustrations to teach him and to encourage him in his own illustrations. When you are sharing your testimony or teaching a class, use these illustrations to add a personal element to your presentation: "Here is how God worked in my life."

God often builds character in our lives by putting us in situations where we are tempted to do the opposite. For example, God may teach you honesty by placing you in a situation where you are tempted to be dishonest.

SUMMARY AND CONCLUSION

When I was in college, I was active in a musical group. I owned about $2,000 worth of the equipment it used. Once when I was preaching 500 miles away, another music group at our school came to my roommate and asked if they could borrow my equipment. He told them, "I'm sure it would be all right, but you have to ask Rick first. I'm sure he will let you use it."

But because I was away, they didn't ask me. They simply came back after my roommate had gone and took the equipment. Later that weekend I called in and was told about my equipment being taken. I got furious. I hung up the phone and was really steamed. I would have loaned it to them had they asked me, but they hadn't, and this was like stealing. I was upset, planning all kinds of things I would say and do when I returned.

In the meantime I had been doing a character quality study on forgiveness. That morning I had read in the Bible: *"Make sure that nobody pays back wrong for wrong, but always try to be kind to each other and to everyone else. Be joyful always; pray continually; give thanks in all circumstances, for this is God's will for you in Christ Jesus"* (1 Thessalonians 5:15–18). I suddenly realized that in order to develop the quality of forgiveness, I had to forgive those people who had taken my equipment, I had to remain joyful, and I had to give thanks for the situation.

So here was a concrete situation that God had brought into my life that was going to help me build the character quality of forgiveness into my practical daily living. It was a tough lesson, but it was part of applying what we learn in Scripture. Writing that down has enabled me to share that experience with others.

HOW TO FILL IN THE CHARACTER QUALITY STUDY FORM

Use the form at the end of this chapter to write down the nine steps of your Bible study. You may reproduce these sections.

Sample Filled-out Form

See the example at the end of this chapter.

Assignment

A good place to start this study would be to go through the lists of qualities found in New Testament passages. Some positive ones are:

- Matthew 5:3–12—the Beatitudes
- Galatians 5:22–23—the fruit of the Spirit
- Philippians 4:4–9—admirable qualities
- 2 Peter 1:5–8—qualities that should increase in our lives

Don't forget to study negative qualities as well, so that you can work on ridding these features from your life. Here are some negative qualities:

- Galatians 5:19–21—a list of the works of the flesh
- 2 Timothy 3:1–5—have nothing to do with these!

On the next page, you will find a list of specific qualities taught throughout the Bible that you should study and work on.

POSITIVE QUALITIES

1. Servanthood
2. Honesty
3. Humility
4. Determination
5. Diligence
6. Faithfulness
7. Availability
8. Teachability
9. Forgiveness
10. Generosity
11. Loyalty
12. Fairness
13. Cooperativeness
14. Discipline
15. Sincerity
16. Contentment

NEGATIVE QUALITIES

1. Laziness
2. A critical spirit
3. Pride
4. Selfishness
5. Unfaithfulness
6. Disrespectfulness
7. Rebelliousness
8. Gossip
9. Being unloving
10. Dishonesty
11. Impatience
12. Worry
13. Fearfulness
14. Lustfulness
15. Bitterness
16. Apathy

Many others may be found in Scripture, but these should get you started. A much longer list of biblical qualities, both negative and positive, is provided in Appendix C in *Rick Warren's Bible Study Methods*, page 259.

For Further Reading

The Building of Character by J. R. Miller (AMG Publishers)
Character Sketches, 2 vols. (Institute of Basic Life Principles)
The Master Bible, edited by J. Wesley Dickson (J. Wesley Dickson & Co.)
The Measure of a Man by Gene Getz (Regal Books)
The Measure of a Woman by Gene Getz (Regal Books)

Character Quality Study Form

1. CHARACTER QUALITY (Boldness)

"An exhibition of courage and fearlessness; bravery; willingness to move ahead confidently in the face of danger."

2. OPPOSITE QUALITY (Timidity, fearfulness)

"To shrink back from a difficult or dangerous circumstance; to be hesitant."

3. SIMPLE WORD STUDY

Old Testament word:

***Bâtah** means "to be confident."*

*Example: Proverbs 28:1 — "The righteous are as **bold** as a lion."*

New Testament words:

***Tharreo** means "to be confident, bold, or daring."*

*Example: Hebrews 13:6 — "So that we may **boldly** say, 'The Lord is my helper, and I will not fear what man shall do unto me'" (KJV)*

***Parrçsiazomai** means "to speak boldly or freely."*

*Example: Acts 19:8 — "Paul entered the synagogue and **spoke boldly** there for three months, arguing persuasively about the kingdom of God."*

Reference tools used:

- ***Young's Analytical Concordance to the Bible***
- ***Vine's Expository Dictionary of New Testament Words***

4. CROSS-REFERENCE INSIGHTS

- *Christ spoke boldly in the face of opposition (John 7:26).*

- *Our confidence and boldness come from knowing that the Lord will help us in difficult situations (Hebrews 13:6).*

- *Peter and John were bold because they had been with Jesus (Acts 4:13).*

- *When the Holy Spirit fills our life, we will be able to speak the Word of God boldly. The first Christians prayed for boldness in witnessing and God answered their prayer by filling them with the Holy Spirit (Acts 4:29–31).*

- *When Christ's love is in us, we will be bold because there is no fear in love. Perfect love casts out all fear (1 John 4:17–18).*

5. SIMPLE BIOGRAPHICAL STUDY

The apostle Paul is a major example of boldness. His entire life seemed to be characterized by this quality:

- *As a young Christian in Damascus, he witnessed boldly for Christ (Acts 9:27).*
- *Everywhere he went, he shared his faith boldly in spite of opposition and persecution:*
  - *in Jerusalem (Acts 9:28–29)*
  - *in Pisidian Antioch (Acts 13:46)*
  - *in Iconium (Acts 14:3)*
  - *in Ephesus (Acts 19:8)*
  - *in Thessalonica (1 Thessalonians 2:2)*
- *He wrote bold letters to the churches (Romans 15:15).*
- *He asked people to pray that he would continually preach and teach with boldness (Ephesians 6:19–20).*
- *His Christian testimony while in prison caused others to speak boldly for Christ (Philippians 1:14).*
- *He even faced death boldly (Philippians 1:20). "According to my earnest expectation and hope, that I shall not be put to shame in anything, but that with all boldness, Christ shall even now, as always, be exalted in my body, whether by life or by death" (NASB).*

6. MEMORY VERSE(S)

"So we say with confidence, 'The Lord is my helper; I will not be afraid. What can man do to me?'" (Hebrews 13:6)

7. A SITUATION OR RELATIONSHIP (where God wants to work on this quality in my life)

I have been afraid to witness to my friend, Ted, who works with me at the office.

8. MY PROJECT

First, I will ask my wife to pray with me about overcoming my timidity in witnessing to Ted. Then, each day this week I will pause before going into the office and ask the Holy Spirit to fill my life and give me boldness to witness to Ted (Acts 4:31).

9. PERSONAL ILLUSTRATION

Monday and Tuesday of this week I prayed for boldness to witness to Ted, but the opportunity just didn't arise. Tuesday night I decided that I needed to be more earnest in my prayers, so I asked my wife to pray with me specifically for a chance to share my faith with Ted on Wednesday.

Wednesday morning, I paused at the office door before going in, and I prayed silently that Ted would sense that I "had been with Jesus," like Peter and John (Acts 4:13). Then I went in and placed my Bible on top of my desk, hoping Ted would recognize it.

During the coffee break, Ted came over to talk to me. He noticed my Bible and said, "Is that a Bible?"

I answered, "It sure is. Have you ever read it?" "Not lately," he said.

I said, "Well I've been reading it a lot lately, and I've discovered some neat things in it." I then shared a brief testimony of what God was doing in my life. Ted seemed mildly interested—at least he wasn't turned off. It's a start, and I thank God for giving me the boldness to go this far.

Character Quality Study Form

1. CHARACTER QUALITY

2. OPPOSITE QUALITY

3. SIMPLE WORD STUDY

4. CROSS-REFERENCE INSIGHTS

5. SIMPLE BIOGRAPHICAL STUDY

6. MEMORY VERSE(S)

7. A SITUATION OR RELATIONSHIP (where God wants to work on this quality in my life)

8. MY PROJECT

9. PERSONAL ILLUSTRATION

TOOLS
for
EFFECTIVE
BIBLE STUDY

Tools for Effective Bible Study

THE PURPOSE OF REFERENCE TOOLS

Christians living in the Western world have an abundance of helpful books that are designed to aid us in our personal Bible study, making use of the latest archeological finds, word studies, and research of great Bible scholars. Bible study tools, however, are not meant to replace the Bible; rather, they help us in studying the Bible itself. Bible study is a skill we need to develop.

Most skills require the use of some kinds of tools. Carpenters need their hammers and saws; artists need their brushes and paints; plumbers need their wrenches. Likewise, serious Bible students will want to take advantage of the available reference tools to help them search the Scriptures effectively. People who try to study the Bible systematically without using good tools will find their job tedious and difficult.

Some Christians hesitate to use reference tools out of fear they will become too dependent on them. Some say piously, "All I need is the Bible." True, but the tools suggested in this section are designed to help you get *into* the Bible. You should not be afraid of using reference tools, for most of these books represent the lifelong studies of dedicated men of God. The insights they received from the Lord can enrich your Bible study immensely and provide information about people, places, and events that you would not find in the Bible alone.

THE TOOLS THEMSELVES

In this section we look at eight types of reference tools that are used in the Bible study methods presented and explained in *Rick Warren's Bible Study Methods.*

Many of these tools are available in electronic format through Bible software programs such as *WORDsearch Bible Software*, *Logos Bible Software*, *QuickVerse Bible Software*, and the excellent, free downloadable Bible program at **www.e-sword.org**. We also recommend you make use of the free resources at **www.youversion.com** and **www.biblegateway.com**.

1. **The Study Bible.** Your first and most important tool is a good study Bible. Some Bibles are more adaptable to personal Bible study than others. A good study Bible should have print large enough for you to read for long periods of time without getting a headache from eyestrain. Also it should have paper thick enough for you to

make notes without the ink running through the paper to the next page. Wide margins are helpful because they allow room for making personal notations. Finally, a study Bible should have a good system of cross-references.

I recommend the *New International Version* (NIV) because exhaustive concordances and various study Bibles are available today in that version. The study Bible includes a general edition as well as versions designed for particular categories of people, such as men, women, teenagers, and people still in their spiritual search for God.

Study Bibles and concordances are also available in the *King James Version* (KJV), but that version's archaic language can be a challenge unless you keep a more recent translation at your side during your Bible study.

2. **Several Recent Translations.** In the past fifty years we have seen the production of many new translations of the Bible that use contemporary English. Though weaknesses exist in every translation, each one makes a unique contribution to a better understanding of the Bible. Many people who were previously not interested in the *King James Version* have begun to read and study the Bible in the more recent translations. The greatest benefit you can receive from these versions is comparing them with one another in your study. The many possible meanings and usages of a word can be found by reading a verse in the various versions and noting the differences.

   Also available today are some "parallel" Bibles, which include several translations side by side in a single volume. This allows you to compare translations quickly without having to lay out 10 Bibles across your desk. In addition to these recent translations, a few well-known paraphrases have been produced. A translation is more of a word-for-word translation from the original language; a paraphrase is what one person believes the original says, which calls for inclusion of their own interpretations in some places. Most translations have been prepared by a group of scholars, while a paraphrase is the work of one man. Paraphrases are fine for occasional light devotional reading, but should not be used for serious Bible study. Use an accurate and respected translation for that.

   Some useful and reliable translations available today are:

   - The *New International Version* (Zondervan)—the most widely used English translation in America.

   - The *New American Standard Bible* (produced by the Lockman Foundation and published by Zondervan and several other publishers)—recognized as one of the most accurate translations that is faithful to the original languages.

- The *Amplified Bible* (produced by the Lockman Foundation and published by Zondervan)—a translation that includes different possible meanings of many words used in the text. It seeks to show the many renderings a Greek or Hebrew word can have, so you can understand the full implications of its usage. (Some say it allows the reader to select his own meanings.) It is helpful in doing word studies, but is not recommended as a regular reading Bible.

- The *New Living Translation* (produced and published by Tyndale House)—a contemporary translation that has a dynamic approach to language similar to that of the NIV. It is a little freer in its language than the NIV, but it is not a paraphrase like its predecessor, *The Living Bible*.

Many other fine translations are available today, so choose the ones with which you will be most comfortable. Two or three different recent Bible translations will get you started.

Two paraphrases that have become popular are *The Living Bible* by Kenneth Taylor (Tyndale) and *The Message* by Eugene Peterson (NavPress).

See **Which Bible Is Right for Me?** on page 178 of this workbook for more information on selecting a Bible.

3. **An Exhaustive Concordance.** By far the most important tool you will need in Bible study next to your study Bible is a concordance geared to your primary Bible version. This tool is a Bible index of the words contained in that version. A number of Bibles have limited concordances at the back, which list only a few of the major words and names. An "exhaustive" concordance lists every usage of every word in the Bible, and gives all the references where that word may be found.

   Exhaustive concordances are available today for various versions of the Bible. They are the descendants, adapted to more recent translations, of the original *Strong's Exhaustive Concordance* (various publishers) that was compiled for the *King James Version*. Two of these are the following:

   - *The Strongest NIV Exhaustive Concordance* (Zondervan)
   - *The Strongest NASB Exhaustive Concordance* (Zondervan)

   In addition, there is *Young's Analytical Concordance to the Bible* (Eerdmans), which, like Strong's, originated in the nineteenth century and is based on the *King James Version*. Young's is better than Strong's for word studies because of the way it is organized. All exhaustive concordances are large, bulky volumes that are fairly expensive, but they are worth every penny you invest in them. You will need a concordance in all but two of the methods presented in *Rick Warren's Bible Study Methods*.

4. **A Bible Dictionary and/or Bible Encyclopedia.** A Bible dictionary explains many of the words, topics, customs, and traditions in the Bible as well as gives historical, geographical, cultural, and archeological information. Background material is also given for each book of the Bible, and short biographies are presented for the major people of both testaments. A Bible encyclopedia is an expanded Bible dictionary with longer articles that deal in greater detail with more subjects. Some of the best are:

    - *Baker Encyclopedia of the Bible*, 2 vols. (Baker)
    - *The Complete Book of When and Where in the Bible* (Tyndale)
    - *Holman Illustrated Bible Dictionary*, rev. ed. (Broadman & Holman)
    - *The Illustrated Bible Dictionary*, 3 vols. (Tyndale)
    - *Nelson's New Illustrated Bible Dictionary* (Nelson)
    - *New Bible Dictionary*, 3rd ed. (Intervarsity Press)
    - *Tyndale Bible Dictionary* (Tyndale)
    - *The Zondervan Pictorial Encyclopedia of the Bible*, 5 vols. (Zondervan)

5. **A Topical Bible.** This tool is similar to a concordance except that it categorizes the verses of the Bible by topics instead of by words. This helps a Bible student because a verse often deals with a topic without ever using the specific word. If you had to rely on your concordance alone, you might miss those verses when studying a topic. For example, if you were to look up the subject "Trinity" in *Nave's Topical Bible*, you would find 83 references listed, even though the actual word does not appear in the Bible.

    Another helpful feature is that the verses under each topic are written out in full, which allows you to scan the key verses on a topic quickly without having to look up each one of them in your Bible. You must note, however, that a topical Bible is not exhaustive, for not every verse related to a topic is listed.

    The standard topical Bible for *The King James Version* is *Nave's Topical Bible* (Moody Press). Billy Graham has said that apart from his Bible this is the book he uses more than any other. For a more contemporary version, see the *Zondervan NIV Nave's Topical Bible*.

6. **A Bible Handbook.** This tool is a combination of an encyclopedia and a commentary in concise form. It is used for quick reference while reading through a particular book of the Bible. Instead of being arranged by topics alphabetically, handbooks are designed to follow the order of the books of the Bible. They give background notes, a brief running commentary, and include maps, charts, archeological notes, and many other helpful facts. The best ones are:

    - *Halley's Bible Handbook with the New International Version* (Zondervan)
    - *Holman Bible Handbook* (Broadman & Holman)

- *The New Unger's Bible Handbook* (Moody Press)
- *Zondervan Handbook to the Bible*, rev. ed. (Zondervan)

7. **A Set of Word Studies.** This is one area where today's Christian has the great privilege of profiting from the work of Bible scholars. Because of the availability of practical reference tools written for the average Christian, you can now study the original words of the Bible without knowing anything about Hebrew or Greek. Some men have spent their lives searching out the full meanings of the original words, then writing about them in simple, comprehensible language.

   A good set of word studies will give you the following information: the original root meaning of the Greek or Hebrew word (its etymology), the various uses of the word throughout the Bible and in similar nonbiblical literature of that historical period, and the frequency with which the word occurs in the Bible.

   These reference tools range from inexpensive one-volume expository dictionaries to very expensive twelve-volume sets. These four are recommended:

   - *The Bible Knowledge Key Word Study: New Testament*, 3 vols. (Victor)
   - *The Bible Knowledge Key Word Study: Old Testament*, 4 vols. (Victor)
   - *Expository Dictionary of Bible Words* (Hendrickson)
   - *Kregel Dictionary of the Bible and Theology* (Kregel)

8. **Commentaries.** A commentary is a scholarly collection of explanatory notes and interpretations on the text of a particular Bible book or section of the Bible. Its purpose is to explain and interpret the meaning of the biblical message by analyzing the words used, background, introduction, grammar and syntax, and relation of that particular book to the rest of the Bible. Used properly, commentaries can greatly increase your understanding of the Bible. Generally, you should not refer to a commentary until *after* you have done your own study. Don't let someone else rob you of the joy of discovering biblical insights on your own. Never let reading a commentary take the place of your personal Bible study.

   Because commentaries are written by men, they are fallible. Sometimes equally able commentators disagree on interpretations of the same biblical text. The best way to use a commentary is to check your own findings in your study with those of the authors/commentators, and discover whether they are solid and evangelical in their commitment to Scripture. Beware of buying and using commentaries written by people who do not regard the Bible as the Word of God.

Commentaries come in all sizes, ranging from one volume covering the whole Bible to multivolume sets. Here are some good one- or two-volume commentaries:

- *Baker Commentary on the Bible* (Baker)
- *Bible Knowledge Commentary*, 2 vols. (Victor)
- *Expositor's Bible Commentary: Abridged Edition*, 2 vols. (Zondervan)
- *Nelson's New Illustrated Bible Commentary* (Nelson)
- *New Bible Commentary: Twenty-First Century Edition* (InterVarsity Press)

Commentary series with more volumes include the following. Some series are incomplete, with some volumes still to be published.

- *The Bible Exposition Commentary*, 4 vols. (Baker)
- *Cornerstone Biblical Commentary*, 18 vols. (Tyndale)
- *Expositor's Bible Commentary*, 13 vols. (Zondervan)
- *Holman New Testament Commentary* (Broadman & Holman)
- *Holman Old Testament Commentary* (Broadman & Holman)
- *New American Commentary*, 44 vols. (Broadman & Holman)
- *The NIV Application Commentary*, 23 vols. Old Testament, 20 vols. New Testament (Zondervan)

A BASIC LIBRARY

A person just beginning personal Bible study should obtain only the basic tools necessary to get started. For the Bible study methods presented in *Rick Warren's Bible Study Methods*, the following compose a basic library:

1. A study Bible
2. Two recent Bible versions
3. An exhaustive concordance
4. A Bible dictionary
5. A topical Bible
6. A Bible handbook
7. A one- or two-volume commentary

A MORE ADVANCED LIBRARY

As you become proficient in your personal Bible study and feel comfortable in using the tools in your basic library, you might want to begin adding advanced tools to your collection. In addition to the above seven tools, the following are recommended:

1. Additional versions and paraphrases
2. A Bible encyclopedia
3. A set of word studies
4. Individual commentaries on Bible books
5. A Bible atlas
6. Old and New Testament surveys
7. Any additional Bible study method books that interest you

Conclusion

At this stage you might be thinking, *That's a lot of books!* You are absolutely right, but think of them as long-term investments in your spiritual life. Many books you buy are read once, then put on the shelf to gather dust. But reference books are used over and over again as you study the Bible, and they can give a lifetime of enjoyment. If you are serious about personal Bible study, you will want to acquire these tools regardless of cost.

Start saving money to buy these tools and begin with the basic library. If you will set a goal of buying one book a month, in a year's time you'll have a respectable and valuable collection of reference tools. You might also consider asking for these as Christmas or birthday gifts. A book that you use is a gift that lasts a lifetime.

Finally, encourage your church to set up a section of Bible study reference tools in its library. The church could purchase the more expensive tools, such as the encyclopedias, word studies, and commentary sets, then make them available to its members. In larger churches, the library could possibly obtain several copies of each tool.

Because the Bible is God's Word, Bible study must have a top priority. With these tools you will be able to dig into the Scriptures effectively, an all-important endeavor that will change your life.

WHICH BIBLE IS RIGHT FOR ME?

"With the great variety of Bibles to choose from, which Bible is right for me?" "What is the difference between the NIV, the NLT, and the NKJV, and what do those initials stand for, anyway?" "Which one is the most accurate?"

"Are they re-writing the Bible? Isn't there something wrong with that?"

These are questions people commonly ask when choosing a Bible. Hopefully, we will answer those questions and help you decide which Bible is right for you.

First, we'll talk about translations: what are their differences; are some better than others? Then we'll look at three categories of Bibles: straight text, Study Bibles, and Application Bibles.

So if you're wondering which Bible is right for you, read on, and set your mind at ease . . .

THE GIFT OF TRANSLATIONS

Bible translations fall into three basic categories: Word-for-Word, Thought-for-Thought, and Paraphrase. Their styles can vary from the highly formal and poetic King James language to the street-level informality of the Message Paraphrase. Even so, almost every translation is put together by large teams of biblical scholars who work from the oldest and best known texts available.

WORD-FOR-WORD

Word-for-Word translations exchange one word in the original language for its English equivalent while strictly following the original mechanics, form, and structure of each sentence. The goal is to change as little as possible. The result is a translation that looks and feels very close to the original, but at times sounds different from the way people talk or write today. Word-for-word Bibles are well suited for detailed study and more in-depth reading.

King James Version (KJV)

This translation was first published in 1611 and has since become the best selling book in history. It's a very precise translation, but it's also very traditional, sounding more like Shakespeare than modern English. It's a translation of historical importance and traditional beauty, but is also very challenging to read.

New King James Version (NKJV)

This translation was made in 1982 to update the language and spelling of the King James so that words like "thee," "thou," and "ye" are no longer used. The detail and precision of the King James was preserved, but the style may still be challenging for some to read.

New American Standard Bible (NASB)

This is one of the most accurate translations for detailed study. Colleges and seminaries frequently recommend this translation for their students. It's fairly challenging in some places because it holds so tightly to original texts. While many people use it for devotional reading, most use it more often for study.

THOUGHT-FOR-THOUGHT

Thought-for-thought translations also work at the level of individual words, but preference is given to the basic thought or idea that the author is intending to communicate. The goal is to make it easier to read. Where a word-for-word translation can be choppy and challenging, the thought-for-thought translation slightly rephrases and better articulates the passage for readers. The result is an accurate translation that flows well, is easy to read, and sounds more modern and lively. These translations are the best choice for general reading and most studies. It is important to note that some thought-for-thought translations, like the New Living Translation, lean more towards communicating the general thought, while others like the New International Version stay closer to communicating the specific word.

New International Version (NIV)

The NIV is the best selling and most widely used Bible translation today. It's a good balanced translation because it's both precise like a word-for-word translation and easy to read like a thought-for-thought translation. For this reason the NIV is popular for both devotional reading and Bible study.

New Living Translation (NLT)

The NLT allows for more creativity in translating from the original text than most other translations. Its very modern language and style helps to clarify the meaning of passages in a new way that's designed to catch the reader's attention.

PARAPHRASE

Paraphrased Bibles are a relatively new type of translation. The goal is to make the Bible easier to understand. The translator looks at the original text, translates it into English, but also rewrites it into his own words and style. In a paraphrase, precise words and immediate thoughts are not as important as communicating the general meaning of the passage. The result is a Bible that is easy to read because it uses simple, common language and the author does a lot of the interpretation for us. Paraphrases are best for seeing familiar passages in a new light, or learning how to share God's Word in your own words. A paraphrase makes a good second Bible, or can be especially helpful for new believers or people who struggle with understanding the Bible. However, it is not a good choice for in-depth study and it could be difficult to use in most small groups.

The Message (The Message)

The Message paraphrase, written by biblical scholar Eugene Peterson, is one of the most current, creative, and understandable Bible paraphrases available. His writing style is enjoyable to read, easy to understand, and makes the most basic of biblical ideas accessible to everyone.

CATEGORIES OF BIBLES

There are three primary categories of Bibles to choose from: straight text, Study Bibles, and Application Bibles.

Because the 66 books of the Bible were written by 40 different authors over a span of nearly 2,000 years and in cultures very different from our own, there's a good chance there are whole sections, ideas, and words that we won't understand! Not only do we ask "What does this mean?" but we also ask "How does this apply to my life today?" Meaning in the Bible is universal, but significance is something that varies from person to person.

Translators and publishers address the unique characteristics of the Bible and our personal needs as readers by putting together special editions of specific translations. These editions are intended to help us discover the meaning of a passage and find its significance in our personal lives. Alongside the translated Bible text, these editions will include a wide assortment of extra material such as: historical notes, definitions of words or terms, maps or diagrams, expert commentary, book introductions, or anything else that would be an aid for understanding the text. Some editions also include suggestions for life application and ways to connect with the meaning on a practical level. Still others include content that is geared specifically toward men, women, students, new believers, etc.

STRAIGHT TEXT

Straight text Bibles are simply the Bible text with little or no additional notes or commentary in the margins. Some readers find margin notes distract them from their flow of reading.

STUDY BIBLES

Study Bibles, such as the *NIV Study Bible*, focus on what we can learn about God, his people, and the Scriptures themselves. They do this by delving into the text and revealing nuances of meaning implied by the original languages, or by adding notes that clarify and amplify the text itself.

APPLICATION BIBLES

Application Bibles (also called Devotional Bibles) focus on the application of biblical concepts or precepts to our daily lives. Application notes use story, analogy, and questions to shed new light on various passages of Scripture.

SO, WHICH BIBLE IS RIGHT FOR ME?

As the years go by, most people pick up a couple of different Bibles and use them for different purposes. You might have one you travel with, or one you use at small group, or one at your desk that you highlight, underline, and write in. But ultimately, the best Bible for you or a friend is going to be whichever translation will be read on a regular basis and whatever type has information that will be helpful and encouraging. Think about where and how the Bible is going to be read most. Look through a few different versions and compare a couple of passages. In the end, don't think about "Which Bible should I get?" but ask yourself "Which Bible do I really want to read?" On the next page is a quick comparison of styles to choose from. The text is Matthew 5:13–16.

KING JAMES VERSION (KJV)

Ye are the salt of the earth: but if the salt have lost his savour, wherewith shall it be salted? It is thenceforth good for nothing, but to be cast out, and to be trodden under foot of men. Ye are the light of the world. A city that is set on an hill cannot be hid. Neither do men light a candle, and put it under a bushel, but on a candlestick; and it giveth light unto all that are in the house. Let your light so shine before men, that they may see your good works, and glorify your Father which is in heaven.

NEW KING JAMES VERSION (NKJV)

"You are the salt of the earth; but if the salt loses its flavor, how shall it be seasoned? It is then good for nothing but to be thrown out and trampled underfoot by men. You are the light of the world. *A city that is set on a hill cannot be hidden. Nor do they light a lamp and put it under a basket, but on a lampstand, and it gives light to all who are in the house.* Let your light so shine before men, that they may see your good works and glorify your Father in heaven."

NEW AMERICAN STANDARD BIBLE (NASB)

"You are the salt of the earth; but if the salt has become tasteless, how can it be made salty again? It is no longer good for anything, except to be thrown out and trampled under foot by men. You are the light of the world. *A city set on a hill cannot be hidden; nor does anyone light a lamp and put it under a basket, but on the lampstand, and it gives light to all who are in the house.* Let your light shine before men in such a way that they may see your good works, and glorify your Father who is in heaven."

NEW INTERNATIONAL VERSION (NIV)

"You are the salt of the earth. But if the salt loses its saltiness, how can it be made salty again? It is no longer good for anything, except to be thrown out and trampled underfoot. You are the light of the world. *A town built on a hill cannot be hidden. Neither do people light a lamp and put it under a bowl.* Instead they put it on its stand, and it gives light to everyone in the house. In the same way, let your light shine before others, that they may see your good deeds and glorify your Father in heaven."

NEW LIVING TRANSLATION (NLT)

"You are the salt of the earth. But what good is salt if it has lost its flavor? Can you make it salty again? It will be thrown out and trampled underfoot as worthless. *You are the light of the world—like a city on a hilltop that cannot be hidden. No one lights a lamp and then puts it under a basket.* Instead, a lamp is placed on a stand, where it gives light to everyone in the house. In the same way, let your good deeds shine out for all to see, so that everyone will praise your heavenly Father."

THE MESSAGE (THE MESSAGE)

"Let me tell you why you are here. You're here to be salt-seasoning that brings out the God-flavors of this earth. If you lose your saltiness, how will people taste godliness? You've lost your usefulness and will end up in the garbage. Here's another way to put it: You're here to be light, bringing out the God-colors in the world. *God is not a secret to be kept.* We're going public with this, as public as a city on a hill. If I make you light-bearers, you don't think I'm going to hide you under a bucket, do you? I'm putting you on a light stand. Now that I've put you there on a hilltop, on a light stand—shine! Keep open house; be generous with your lives. By opening up to others, you'll prompt people to open up with God, this generous Father in heaven."

SMALL GROUP RESOURCES

Help for Hosts

Tips for New Hosts

CONGRATULATIONS! As the host of your small group, you have responded to the call to help shepherd Jesus' flock. Few other tasks in the family of God surpass the contribution you will be making. As you prepare to facilitate your group, whether it is one session or the entire series, here are a few thoughts to keep in mind.

Remember you are not alone. God knows everything about you, and he knew you would be asked to facilitate your group. Even though you may not feel ready, this is common for all good hosts. God promises, *"I will never leave you; I will never abandon you"* (Hebrews 13:5 GNT). Whether you are facilitating for one evening, several weeks, or a lifetime, you will be blessed as you serve.

1. **DON'T TRY TO DO IT ALONE.** Pray right now for God to help you build a healthy team. If you can enlist a co-host to help you shepherd the group, you will find your experience much richer. This is your chance to involve as many people as you can in building a healthy group. All you have to do is ask people to help. You'll be surprised at the response.

2. **BE FRIENDLY AND BE YOURSELF.** God wants to use your unique gifts and temperament. Be sure to greet people at the door with a big smile . . . this can set the mood for the whole gathering. Remember, they are taking as big a step to show up at your house as you are to host a small group! Don't try to do things exactly like another host; do them in a way that fits you. Admit when you don't have an answer and apologize when you make a mistake. Your group will love you for it and you'll sleep better at night.

3. **PREPARE FOR YOUR MEETING AHEAD OF TIME.** Review the session and write down your responses to each question. Pay special attention to the **Putting It Into Practice** exercises that ask group members to do something other than engage in discussion. These exercises will help your group live what the Bible teaches, not just talk about it.

4. **PRAY FOR YOUR GROUP MEMBERS BY NAME.** Before you begin your session, take a few moments and pray for each member by name. You may want to review the **Small Group Prayer and Praise Report** at least once a week. Ask God to use your time together to touch the heart of each person in your group. Expect God to lead you to whomever he wants you to encourage or challenge in a special way. If you listen, God will surely lead.

5. **WHEN YOU ASK A QUESTION, BE PATIENT.** Someone will eventually respond. Sometimes people need a moment or two of silence to think about the question. If silence doesn't bother you, it won't bother anyone else. After someone responds, affirm the response with a simple "thanks" or "great answer." Then ask, "How about somebody else?" or "Would someone who hasn't shared like to add anything?" Be sensitive to new people or reluctant members who aren't ready to say, pray, or do anything. If you give them a safe setting, they will blossom over time. If someone in your group is a wallflower who sits silently through every session, consider talking to them privately and encouraging them to participate. Let them know how important they are to you—that they are loved and appreciated, and that the group would value their input. Remember, still water often runs deep.

6. **PROVIDE TRANSITIONS BETWEEN QUESTIONS.** Ask if anyone would like to read the paragraph or Bible passage. Don't call on anyone, but ask for a volunteer, and then be patient until someone begins. Be sure to thank the person who reads aloud.

7. **BREAK INTO SMALLER GROUPS OCCASIONALLY.** With a greater opportunity to talk in a small circle, people will connect more with the study, apply more quickly what they're learning, and ultimately get more out of their small group experience. A small circle also encourages a quiet person to participate and tends to minimize the effects of a more vocal or dominant member.

8. **SMALL CIRCLES ARE ALSO HELPFUL DURING PRAYER TIME.** People who are unaccustomed to praying aloud will feel more comfortable trying it with just two or three others. Also, prayer requests won't take as much time, so circles will have more time to actually pray. When you gather back with the whole group, you can have one person from each circle briefly update everyone on the prayer requests from their subgroups. The other great aspect of subgrouping is that it fosters leadership development. As you ask people in the group to facilitate discussion or to lead a prayer circle, it gives them a small leadership step that can build their confidence.

9. **ROTATE FACILITATORS OCCASIONALLY.** You may be perfectly capable of hosting each time, but you will help others grow in their faith and gifts if you give them opportunities to host the group.

10. **PREPARE YOUR HEART.** Before your first opportunity to lead, read each of the six passages listed below as a devotional exercise to help prepare you with a shepherd's heart.

Matthew 9:36–38 (NIV)

When [Jesus] saw the crowds, he had compassion on them, because they were harassed and helpless, like sheep without a shepherd. Then he said to his disciples, "The harvest is plentiful but the workers are few. Ask the Lord of the harvest, therefore, to send out workers into his harvest field."

John 10:14–15 (NIV)

"I am the good shepherd; I know my sheep and my sheep know me—just as the Father knows me and I know the Father—and I lay down my life for the sheep."

1 Peter 5:2–4 (NIV)

Be shepherds of God's flock that is under your care, serving as overseers—not because you must, but because you are willing, as God wants you to be; not greedy for money, but eager to serve; not lording it over those entrusted to you, but being examples to the flock. And when the Chief Shepherd appears, you will receive the crown of glory that will never fade away.

Philippians 2:1–5 (NIV)

If you have any encouragement from being united with Christ, if any comfort from his love, if any fellowship with the Spirit, if any tenderness and compassion, then make my joy complete by being like-minded, having the same love, being one in spirit and purpose. Do nothing out of selfish ambition or vain conceit, but in humility consider others better than yourselves. Each of you should look not only to your own interests, but also to the interests of others. Your attitude should be the same as that of Christ Jesus.

Hebrews 10:23–25 (NIV)

Let us hold unswervingly to the hope we profess, for he who promised is faithful. And let us consider how we may spur one another on toward love and good deeds. Let us not give up meeting together, as some are in the habit of doing, but let us encourage one another—and all the more as you see the Day approaching.

1 Thessalonians 2:7–8, 11–12 (NIV)

But we were gentle among you, like a mother caring for her little children. We loved you so much that we were delighted to share with you not only the Gospel of God but our lives as well, because you had become so dear to us. For you know that we dealt with each of you as a father deals with his own children, encouraging, comforting and urging you to live lives worthy of God, who calls you into his kingdom and glory.

Frequently Asked Questions

HOW LONG WILL THIS GROUP MEET?

This study is six sessions long. We encourage your group to add a seventh session for a celebration. In your final session, each group member may decide if he or she desires to continue on for another study. At that time you may also want to do some informal evaluation, discuss your **Small Group Guidelines**, and decide which study you want to do next. We recommend you visit our website at **PastorRick.com** for more video-based small group studies.

WHO IS THE HOST?

The host is the person who coordinates and facilitates your group meetings. In addition to a host, we encourage you to select one or more group members to lead your group discussions. Several other responsibilities can be rotated, including serving refreshments, overseeing prayer requests, facilitating worship, or keeping up with those who miss a meeting. Shared ownership in the group helps everybody grow.

WHERE DO WE FIND NEW GROUP MEMBERS?

Recruiting new members can be a challenge for groups, especially new groups with just a few people, or existing groups that lose a few people along the way. We encourage you to use the **Circles of Life** diagram on page 194 of this workbook to brainstorm a list of people from your workplace, church, school, neighborhood, family, and so on. Then pray for the people on each member's list. Allow each member to invite several people from their list. Some groups fear that newcomers will interrupt the intimacy that members have built over time. However, groups that welcome newcomers generally gain strength with the infusion of new blood. Remember, the next person you add just might become a friend for eternity. Logistically, groups find different ways to add members. Some groups remain permanently open, while others choose to open periodically, such as at the beginning or end of a study. If your group becomes too large for easy, face-to-face conversations, you can subgroup, forming a second discussion group in another room.

HOW DO WE HANDLE THE CHILDCARE NEEDS IN OUR GROUP?

Childcare needs must be handled very carefully. This is a sensitive issue. We suggest you seek creative solutions as a group. One common solution is to have the adults meet in the living room and share the cost of a baby sitter (or two) who can be with the kids in another part of the house. Another popular option is to have one home for the kids and a second home (close by) for the adults. If desired, the adults could rotate the responsibility of providing a lesson for the kids. This last option is great with school-age kids and can be a huge blessing to families.

Small Group Guidelines

It's a good idea for every group to put words to their shared values, expectations, and commitments. Such guidelines will help you avoid unspoken agendas and unmet expectations. We recommend you discuss your guidelines during Session 1 in order to lay the foundation for a healthy group experience. Feel free to modify anything that does not work for your group.

We agree to the following values:

CLEAR PURPOSE	To grow healthy spiritual lives by building a healthy small group community
GROUP ATTENDANCE	To give priority to the group meeting (call if I am absent or late)
SAFE ENVIRONMENT	To create a safe place where people can be heard and feel loved (no quick answers, snap judgments, or simple fixes)
BE CONFIDENTIAL	To keep anything that is shared strictly confidential and within the group
CONFLICT RESOLUTION	To avoid gossip and to immediately resolve any concerns by following the principles of Matthew 18:15–17
SPIRITUAL HEALTH	To give group members permission to speak into my life and help me live a healthy, balanced spiritual life that is pleasing to God
LIMIT OUR FREEDOM	To limit our freedom by not serving or consuming alcohol during small group meetings or events so as to avoid causing a weaker brother or sister to stumble (1 Corinthians 8:1–13; Romans 14:19–21)
WELCOME NEWCOMERS	To invite friends who might benefit from this study and warmly welcome newcomers
BUILDING RELATIONSHIPS	To get to know the other members of the group and pray for them regularly
OTHER	______________________________
	______________________________

We have also discussed and agree on the following items:

CHILD CARE ______________________________

STARTING TIME ______________________________

ENDING TIME ______________________________

If you haven't already done so, take a few minutes to fill out the **Small Group Calendar** on page 195.

Circles of Life: Small Group Connections

DISCOVER WHO YOU CAN CONNECT IN COMMUNITY

Use this chart to help carry out one of the values in the **Small Group Guidelines**—to "Welcome Newcomers."

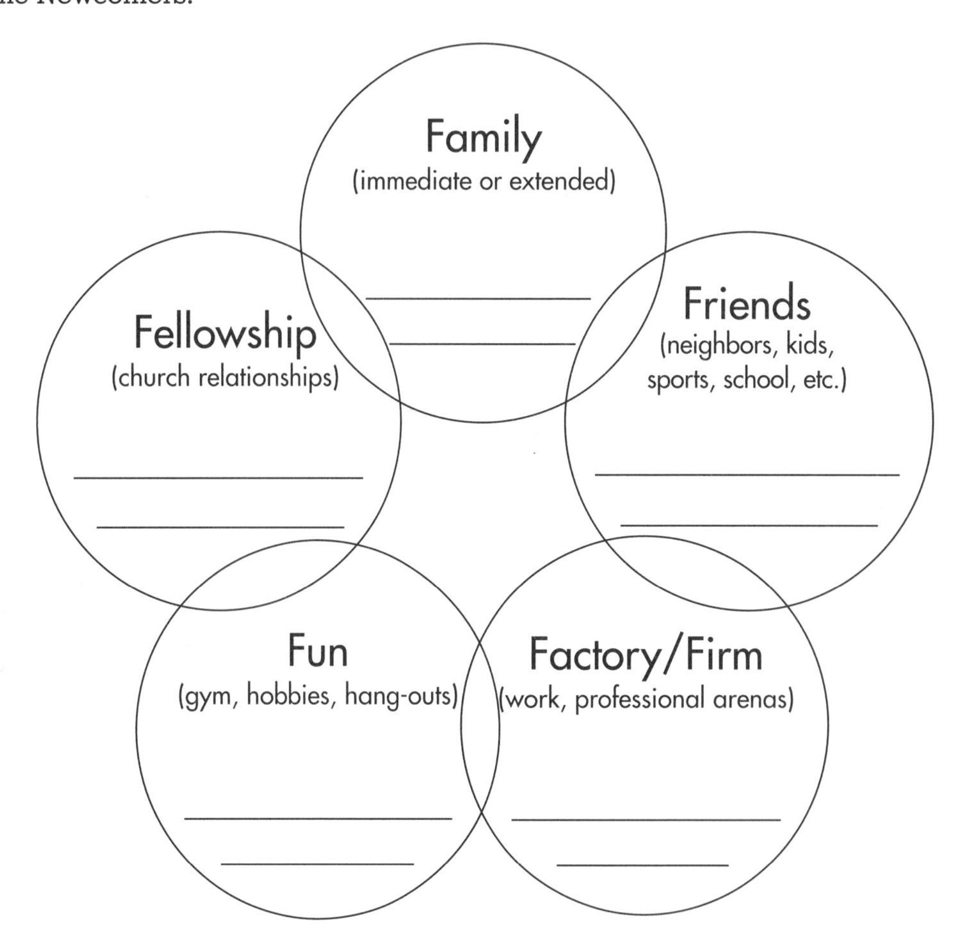

Follow this simple three-step process:

1. List one to two people in each circle.
2. Prayerfully select one person or couple from your list and tell your group about them.
3. Give them a call and invite them to your next meeting. Over fifty percent of those invited to a small group say, "Yes!"

Small Group Calendar

Healthy groups share responsibilities and group ownership. It might take some time for this to develop. Shared ownership ensures that responsibility for the group doesn't fall to one person. Use the calendar to keep track of social events, mission projects, birthdays, or days off. Complete this calendar at your first or second meeting. Planning ahead will increase attendance and shared ownership.

DATE	PERSON	LOCATION	FACILITATOR	SNACK OR MEAL

Small Group Prayer and Praise Report

This is a place where you can write each other's requests for prayer. You can also make a note when God answers a prayer. Pray for each other's requests. If you're new to group prayer, it's okay to pray silently or to pray by using just one sentence:

"God, please help ________________ to ____________________."

DATE	PERSON	PRAYER REQUEST	PRAISE REPORT

DATE	PERSON	PRAYER REQUEST	PRAISE REPORT

Other Resources

Open Doors: A Year of Daily Devotions

A 365-day devotional from Pastor Rick Warren.

Open the door to greater intimacy with God and experience the love, trust, and freedom that comes from a deeper relationship with him. Discover God's wisdom to resolve conflict, conquer fear, reduce stress, build healthy relationships, overcome temptation, and so much more.

You'll be encouraged, inspired, and equipped to live out God's plan and purpose for your life.

Walk through the doors God has for you today with this devotional!

40 Days of Prayer Study

Taught by Pastor Rick Warren

Most people are struggling with a difficult situation or circumstance. They need a breakthrough in their life. Whether it's praying for a breakthrough in a marriage, health, finances, or relationships, persistent prayer is how God moves to transform people's lives.

Sessions include:

- The Purpose of Prayer
- How to Pray with Confidence
- The Pattern for Prayer – Part One
- The Pattern for Prayer – Part Two
- Praying for a Breakthrough
- How to Pray in a Crisis
- BONUS: Why Doesn't God Always Answer the First Time I Pray?

AWESOME: Building Great Relationships Study

Taught by Pastor Rick Warren

This 4-week study will teach you why marriage matters and how God designed it to make you holy, the four traits of awesome families, the six golden rules of awesome friendships, and how to build a friendship with God and make him your priority.

Sessions include:

- Fighting for an Awesome Marriage
- Fighting for an Awesome Family
- Fighting for Awesome Friendships
- Becoming Best Friends with God
- BONUS: The Seasons of Marriage

What On Earth Am I Here For? Study

Taught by Pastor Rick Warren

This 6-session study will teach you why God created you and how you can discover your identity, meaning, purpose, significance, and destiny.

Sessions include:

- You Matter to God
- You Were Planned for God's Pleasure
- You Were Planned for God's Family
- You Were Created to Become Like Christ
- You Were Shaped to Serve God
- You Were Made for a Mission

To order resources for your church, visit www.Pastors.com

To order resources for your personal study, visit www.PastorRick.com

Answer Key

Session One

The ultimate purpose of the Bible is to CHANGE OUR LIVES.
Ask the RIGHT QUESTIONS.
Write down YOUR OBSERVATIONS.
Don't just interpret it, APPLY IT.
I only believe the parts of the Bible that I ACTUALLY DO.
Study it SYSTEMATICALLY.
Read it OVER AND OVER AGAIN.
You can summarize the devotional study method in one word: MEDITATE.

Session Two

We give DEVOTION to God.
God DESERVES our devotion.
God DESIRES our devotion.
We get DIRECTION from God.
We gain DELIGHT in God.
We grow MORE LIKE God.
Start with the proper ATTITUDES.
Come with EXPECTANCY.
Come with REVERENCE.
Come with ALERTNESS.
Come with WILLINGNESS to obey.
Select a specific TIME.
The best time is when you ARE AT YOUR BEST.
Choose a special PLACE.
Follow a simple PLAN.
Wait ON GOD.
Pray BRIEFLY.
Read A SECTION OF SCRIPTURE.
MEDITATE and MEMORIZE.
Write down WHAT GOD SHOWS YOU.
Have YOUR TIME OF PRAYER.

Session Three

Knowledge produces PRIDE.
Knowledge requires ACTION.
Knowledge increases RESPONSIBILITY.
It requires SERIOUS THINKING.
Satan FIGHTS IT VICIOUSLY.
We naturally RESIST CHANGE.
What did it MEAN THEN?
What is the TIMELESS TRUTH?
How does it APPLY NOW?
S – Is there a SIN to confess?
P – Is there a PROMISE to claim?
A – Is there an ATTITUDE to change?
C – Is there a COMMAND to obey?
E – Is there an EXAMPLE to follow?
P – Is there a PRAYER to pray?
E – Is there an ERROR to avoid?
T – Is there a TRUTH to believe?
S – Is there SOMETHING to praise God for?

Session Four

The problem of DISCIPLINE . . .
The Battle of the BLANKETS
Go to bed ON TIME.
Get up IMMEDIATELY.
Be aware of QUIET TIME ROBBERS.
Go to bed with SCRIPTURE on your mind.
The problem of DRY SPELLS . . .
The Battle of the BLAHS
DISOBEDIENCE
Your PHYSICAL condition
Trying to DO TOO MUCH in a hurry
Being in a RUT
Not sharing your INSIGHTS with others
The problem of DISTRACTIONS . . .
The Battle of the BRAIN
Be sure you are thoroughly AWAKE.
Read and pray ALOUD.
WALK while praying.

Keep a NOTEPAD handy.
The problem of DISCOURAGEMENT . . .
The Battle of BUSYNESS
Make a COVENANT with God.
Put it into your WEEKLY SCHEDULE.
Be prepared for the devil's EXCUSES and ATTACKS.
Leave your Bible OPEN.
Rely on the POWER OF GOD.

Session Five

Memorizing Scripture helps me RESIST TEMPTATION.
Memorizing Scripture helps me make WISE DECISIONS.
Memorizing Scripture STRENGTHENS ME when I'm under stress.
Memorizing Scripture COMFORTS ME when I'm sad.
Memorizing Scripture helps me WITNESS TO UNBELIEVERS.
Pick a VERSE.
Say the VERSE REFERENCE before and after the verse.
Read the verse ALOUD many times.
Break the verse into NATURAL PHRASES.
Emphasize KEY WORDS in each phrase.
Always memorize the verse WORD PERFECT.
PERSONAL—write it in the first person
PRACTICAL—something specific you can do
POSSIBLE—something you know you can accomplish
PROVABLE—measurable so you'll know when you have done it; set a deadline

Session Six

Make a DECISION.
Make a DECLARATION.
Make a DETERMINATION.
DOUBLE-UP.
DEPEND on God.
FAITH and the HOLY SPIRIT are necessary for proper interpretation.
The BIBLE is its own best COMMENTARY.
Read the OLD TESTAMENT with the NEW TESTAMENT in mind, and read the NEW TESTAMENT with the OLD TESTAMENT in mind.
Always interpret UNCLEAR passages in the light of CLEAR passages.
Don't form a DOCTRINE based solely on a HISTORICAL EVENT.
Don't interpret SCRIPTURE based on PERSONAL EXPERIENCES; instead, interpret PERSONAL EXPERIENCES based on SCRIPTURE.

Memory Verses

SESSION 1

Let the word of Christ dwell in you richly.

Colossians 3:16 (NIV)

SESSION 2

Open my eyes that I may see wonderful things in your law.

Psalm 119:18 (NIV)

SESSION 3

Do not merely listen to the word, and so deceive yourselves. Do what it says.

James 1:22 (NIV)

SESSION 4

I have hidden your word in my heart that I might not sin against you.

Psalm 119:11 (NIV)

SESSION 5

Therefore, everyone who hears these words of mine and puts them into practice is like a wise man who built his house on the rock.

Matthew 7:24 (NIV)

SESSION 6

Your word is a lamp to my feet and a light for my path.

Psalm 119:105 (NIV)